AS RevisionNotes

Biology

• Alan Morris • Margaret Baker •

Series editor: Jayne de Courcy

William Collins' dream of knowledge for all began with the publication of his first book in 1819. A self-educated mill worker, he not only enriched millions of lives, but also founded a flourishing publishing house. Today, staying true to this spirit, Collins books are packed with inspiration, innovation and practical expertise. They place you at the centre of a world of possibility and give you exactly what you need to explore it.

Collins. Do more.

Published by Collins
An imprint of HarperCollins*Publishers*
77–85 Fulham Palace Road
Hammersmith
London
W6 8JB

Browse the complete Collins catalogue at
www.collinseducation.com

© HarperCollins*Publishers* Limited 2006

10 9 8 7 6 5 4 3 2 1

ISBN-13 978 0 00 720685 8
ISBN-10 0 00 720685 2

British Library Cataloguing in Publication Data
A Catalogue record for this publication is available from the British Library.

Edited by Pat Winter
Production by Katie Butler
Series design by Sally Boothroyd
Illustrated by Kathy Baxendale
Index compiled by Joan Dearnley
Printed and bound by Printing Express, Hong Kong

You might also like to visit
www.harpercollins.co.uk
The book lover's website

CONTENTS

HOW THIS BOOK WILL HELP YOU

We have planned this book to make your revision as easy and effective as possible.

Here's how:

SHORT, ACCESSIBLE NOTES THAT YOU CAN INTEGRATE INTO YOUR REVISION FILE

Collins Revision Notes AS Biology has been prepared by top examiners who know exactly what you need to revise in order to be successful.

You can *either* base your revision on this book *or* you can tear off the notes and integrate them into your own revision file. This will ensure that you have the best possible notes to revise from.

STUDENT-FRIENDLY PRESENTATION

The notes use lots of visual aids – diagrams, tables, charts, etc. – so the content is easier to remember.

There is also systematic use of colour to help you revise:

MUST REMEMBER
Red panels stress ideas that you must express clearly in order to gain full marks.

MUST TAKE CARE
Purple panels highlight particularly tricky areas.

– Red type identifies key biology terms.
– Green type is used for key definitions.
– Yellow highlight emphasises important words and phrases.

CONTENT MATCHED TO YOUR SPECIFICATION

This book covers the AS course for three specifications:
AQA Biology Specification A
AQA Biology Specification B
AQA Human Biology

You need to revise the whole of Section I whichever of these specifications you are following. Section II contains additional topics for AQA Biology Specification A. Section III contains additional topics for AQA Biology Specification B. Section IV contains additional topics for AQA Human Biology.

GUIDANCE ON EXAM TECHNIQUE

This book concentrates on providing you with the best possible revision notes.

Knowing the facts is vital – but you may also want help with answering exam questions. That is why we have also produced an exam practice book which you can use alongside these Revision Notes: *Collins Exam Practice AS Biology.*

Using both these books will ensure that you achieve the highest possible grade in your AS Biology exams.

BIOLOGICAL MOLECULES

There are three groups of biological molecules:

- Carbohydrates
- Proteins
- Lipids (triglycerides)

CARBOHYDRATES

MAIN POINTS

Made of the elements	Special features	Polymers	Different forms
Carbon Oxygen Hydrogen (C, H, O)	Two atoms of hydrogen to each atom of oxygen	Monomers of α-glucose form starch and glycogen Monomers of β-glucose form cellulose	Monosaccharides glucose, fructose Disaccharides maltose, sucrose, lactose Polysaccharides starch, glycogen, cellulose

DETAIL

Type of sugar	Number of carbon atoms per molecule	Formula	Example	Where it is found
Triose	3	$C_3H_6O_3$	Triose phosphate (TP)	Intermediate compound in respiration and photosynthesis
Pentose	5	$C_5H_{10}O_5$	Ribose	Sugar in RNA
Hexose	6	$C_6H_{12}O_6$	Glucose	Respiratory substrate; monomer used to make starch, glycogen, cellulose

STRUCTURAL FORMULAS

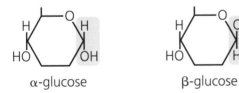

α-glucose   β-glucose

- This is the only difference.

α-glucose and β-glucose are **isomers**. They both have the formula $C_6H_{12}O_6$ but the atoms are organised in different ways.

MUST REMEMBER

For AQA B or OCR specifications, learn the full structural formula:

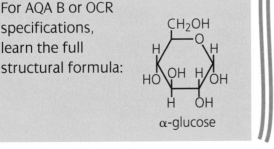

α-glucose

- Hexose sugars can join together by a **condensation reaction**.
- Water is given out.
- Sugars are held together by **glycosidic bonds** (these are **strong bonds**).

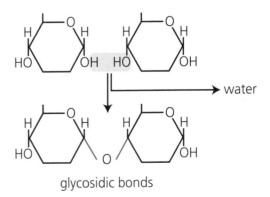

glycosidic bonds

When glycosidic bonds break by a **hydrolysis reaction**, water is added and monosaccharides are formed.

PROTEINS

MAIN POINTS

Made of the elements	Special features	Polymers	Different forms
Carbon Oxygen Hydrogen Nitrogen (C, H, O, N)	Proteins can also contain atoms of sulphur.	Monomers of **amino acid** join together to form: • dipeptides • peptides • polypeptides Chain length increases down the list. When the polypeptide is modified, it forms a **protein**.	**(A) Primary structure** Chain of amino acids is held together by **peptide bonds**. **(B) Secondary structure** Folding of primary structure is held together by **hydrogen bonds**. **(C) Tertiary structure** Further folding of the secondary structure is held together by **hydrogen**, **ionic** and **disulphide** bonds. **(D) Quaternary structure** Two or more tertiary proteins are joined together.

(A) Primary structure

(B) Secondary structure

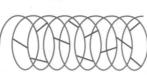

(C) Tertiary structure

(D) Quaternary structure

DETAIL

- All proteins are polymers.
- The monomer is an amino acid.
- There are 20 different forms of amino acid.
- Each amino acid has a common structure with one different chemical group (given the letter **R**), making it unique.

R — variable group

common to all amino acids

amino group   carboxyl group

- The **amino group** of one amino acid joins with the **carboxyl group** of another.
- They are held together by a **peptide bond (which is a strong bond)**.
- This is a **condensation reaction**.
- A **hydrolysis** reaction will break the bond.

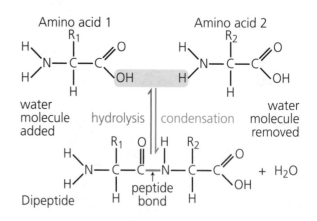

The **dipeptide** still has an amino group at one end and a carboxyl group at the other, so another amino acid can join at either end to form a longer chain.

MUST REMEMBER

- The R group could be replaced with a specific group, for example:
  - R_1 could be H = the amino acid glycine.
  - R_2 could be CH_3 = the amino acid alanine.
- This makes no difference to how two amino acids join.

LIPIDS (TRIGLYCERIDES)

MAIN POINTS

Made of the elements	Special features	Polymers	Different forms
Carbon Oxygen Hydrogen (C, H, O)	More than two hydrogen atoms to each oxygen atom	No polymers	Triglyceride (There are other forms but we do not need to know them.)

DETAILS

Components	Formula	
One glycerol molecule is used to form a triglyceride.	$C_3H_8O_3$	Glycerol is always present.

Three fatty acid molecules are used to form a triglyceride.

- The three fatty acids used can be the same or different.

Saturated fatty acid

Saturated fatty acids are when all the bonds in the 'tail' are single.

Unsaturated fatty acid

Unsaturated fatty acids are when there is at least one double bond in the 'tail'.

Simplified fatty acid

The COOH group is the only part that remains the same.

The rest is variable, so we call it R.

MUST REMEMBER

Look at the formula for a triose sugar $C_3H_6O_3$ and a glycerol $C_3H_8O_3$. In the triose sugar, the ratio of hydrogen to oxygen is 2:1, but in the glycerol there are more than 2 hydrogen atoms per oxygen.

FORMING A TRIGLYCERIDE

- Glycerol and three fatty acids join together by a **condensation reaction**.
- They are held together by **ester bonds** (these are **strong bonds**).
- A **hydrolysis** reaction will break a triglyceride into fatty acids and glycerol.

Fatty acid comes close to glycerol

Condensation reaction occurs

Water molecule is removed

An ester bond is formed

Three ester bonds are formed

Triglyceride is formed

BIOCHEMICAL TESTS

Substance	Reagent/Test	Method	Result	Conclusion
Reducing sugars e.g. glucose	Benedict's	Add Benedict's ↓ Heat	Goes **orange/red** Remains **blue**	Reducing sugar present Reducing sugar NOT present
Non-reducing sugars e.g. sucrose	Hydrochloric acid (HCl) Benedict's	Add HCl ↓ Heat ↓ Allow to cool ↓ Neutralise ↓ Add Benedict's ↓ Heat	Goes **orange/red** Remains **blue**	Non-reducing sugar present Non-reducing sugar NOT present
Starch	Iodine solution	Add iodine solution	Goes **blue-black** Remains yellow/orange	Starch present Starch NOT present
Protein	Biuret	Add Biuret A ↓ Add Biuret B	Goes **purple** Remains **blue**	Protein present Protein NOT present
Lipid	Emulsion test	Add ethanol ↓ Shake ↓ Decant into water	White layer = emulsion on top	Lipid present

MUST REMEMBER

- A reducing sugar test does NOT test for specific sugars.
- A non-reducing sugar test does NOT test for specific sugars.
- A non-reducing sugar test is only done after a reducing sugar test has remained blue.
- Must not confuse Benedict's with Biuret.

CELLS

TYPES OF CELL

- Simple cells such as bacteria (members of the kingdom prokaryotae) are called **prokaryotic cells**.
- Cells in all other organisms (members of the kingdoms animalia, plantae, fungi and protoctista) are **eukaryotic cells**.

MUST TAKE CARE . . .

In exam questions, must look out for named cells such as:

- the bacterium *E. coli* or
- a mesophyll cell from a leaf

Must make sure to pick up the key word, **bacterium** or **plant**, then it will be easy to describe the differences.

The main differences between prokaryotic cells and eukaryotic cells:

Characteristic	Prokaryotic cell	Eukaryotic cell
Size	Small – about 5 μm	Large – about 50 μm
Cell wall	Wall made of **murein**	Plants have walls made of **cellulose**. Fungi have cell walls made of **chitin**.
Organelles	No membrane-bound organelles Small (70S) **ribosomes** free in cytoplasm	**Membrane-bound organelles** such as mitochondria, chloroplasts, golgi apparatus, lysosomes Large (80S) **ribosomes** present, some free, some attached to endoplasmic reticulum
Nucleus	Not present	**Nucleus** present, enclosed by a double membrane (nuclear envelope)
Genetic material	Single circular DNA molecule, no chromosomes present. Small rings of DNA can be present – **plasmids**.	Many linear DNA molecules forming **chromosomes**

For practice in answering AS Biology questions, why not use *Collins Exam Practice AS Biology*?

ORGANELLES

Plants and animals are multicellular organisms made up of eukaryotic cells which contain many organelles. Each organelle has a different function:

Organelle	Structure	Function
Plasma membrane		Is partially permeable and controls the entry and exit of materials
Nucleus		Houses the **genetic material (DNA)** and separates it from the active enzymes in the cytoplasm
Mitochondrion		Site of **aerobic respiration** (the production of ATP)
Endoplasmic reticulum (ER) • Rough ER • Smooth ER		Membrane bound sacs and tubes which: • transport proteins • are the site of lipid synthesis
Ribosome		Site of protein synthesis
Golgi apparatus		Stores and chemically modifies substances produced in the cell
Vesicle		Transports the products of Golgi apparatus to the cell surface for **secretion**
Lysosome		Vesicle containing **digestive enzymes**, made by Golgi apparatus

SPECIFIC ORGANELLES

Some organelles are found in either plant or animals cells:

	Organelle	Function
Only found in animal cells	Microvilli	Finger-like projections in an area of the plasma membrane which **increase its surface area**
Only found in plant cells	Cellulose cell wall	To provide support and to stop the cell from bursting (The wall is completely permeable, even to water.)
	Chloroplast	The site of **photosynthesis**
	Large central vacuole	To store nutrients such as sucrose and amino acids

TRANSPORT ACROSS MEMBRANES

MEMBRANE TYPES

All membranes are basically the same:
- Plasma membrane – outside surface of all cells
- Membranes surrounding organelles, including mitochondria, chloroplasts
- Membranes making up organelles, including endoplasmic reticulum

They are all made of:
- phospholipid
- protein
- carbohydrate

Membranes are described by the **fluid** (phospholipid molecules move) **mosaic** (protein molecules are embedded in the membrane) **model**.

BASIC STRUCTURE AND FUNCTION

Parts of the membrane	Notes
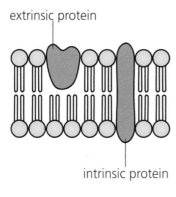 phospholipid bilayer — head (glycerol + phosphate) = hydrophilic — tail (2 fatty acids) = hydrophobic	• It is a bilayer – has two layers. • Head attracts water. • Tail repels water. **MUST TAKE CARE** Musn't use the terms 'love' or 'hate' as molecules have no emotions. **FUNCTION** • Framework to attach other molecules • Waterproofing
extrinsic protein intrinsic protein	• Extrinsic proteins are embedded in one layer. Extrinsic protein could be in either layer. • Intrinsic proteins span both layers. **FUNCTION** • Carry molecules across membrane • Act as antigens • Are hormone receptors
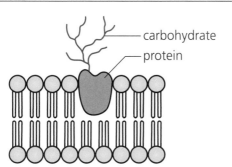 — carbohydrate — protein	• Carbohydrate is always attached to protein. • Carbohydrate is always embedded in the outside layer. **FUNCTION** • Allows recognition of cell

TRANSPORT THROUGH MEMBRANES

Notes	How it happens

SIMPLE DIFFUSION

It occurs in both directions –
therefore in and out of cell or organelle.

- There is a net movement down a concentration gradient.
- Kinetic energy of molecule causes movement.
- The cell does not provide the energy – passive.
- It is slow.

High concentration

Low concentration

Net effect

FACILITATED DIFFUSION

**It occurs in both directions –
therefore in and out of cell or organelle.**

- There is a net movement down a concentration gradient.
- Kinetic energy of molecules causes movement.
- The cell does not provide the energy – passive.
- It is helped (facilitated) by a **protein carrier**. The carrier molecule is moved by the kinetic energy of the moving molecule.
- It is fast.

High concentration

Low concentration

protein carrier

Net effect

ACTIVE TRANSPORT

**Occurs in one direction –
either in or out of cell or organelle.**

- It occurs against a concentration gradient.
- It requires a **protein carrier**.
- The cell provides the energy – active.
- The protein carrier is moved by energy from the cell.
  ATP is broken down to ADP and phosphate, releasing **energy** for active transport.
- It is fast.

Low concentration

High concentration

protein carrier

Net effect

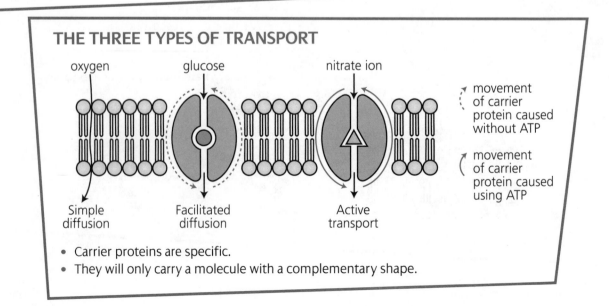

THE THREE TYPES OF TRANSPORT

oxygen · glucose · nitrate ion

Simple diffusion · Facilitated diffusion · Active transport

- - - movement of carrier protein caused without ATP

⌐ movement of carrier protein caused using ATP

- Carrier proteins are specific.
- They will only carry a molecule with a complementary shape.

FICK'S LAW

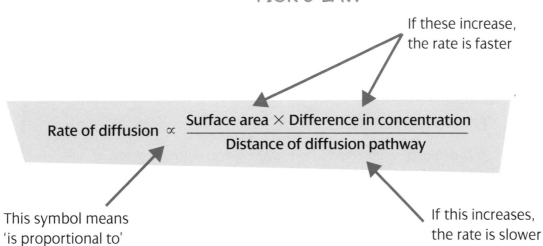

If these increase, the rate is faster

Rate of diffusion ∝ $\dfrac{\text{Surface area} \times \text{Difference in concentration}}{\text{Distance of diffusion pathway}}$

This symbol means 'is proportional to'

If this increases, the rate is slower

MUST TAKE CARE

If asked to write Fick's law, must not forget that it represents the rate of diffusion. Without that, the right-hand side of the equation is meaningless.

Must never say 'across' a concentration gradient, but must always say 'down' a concentration gradient.

CHANGING THE VARIABLES

Variable	When variable is increased	Effect on diffusion
Surface area	There are more places to cross the membrane.	Faster rate
Difference in concentration	More molecules move in one direction.	Faster rate
The concentration alone has no effect on the rate of diffusion.	Molecules move in both directions. The overall rate depends on how many move 'in' compared with how many move 'out'.	
Distance of diffusion pathway	Molecules have further to travel.	Slower rate
The distance across the membrane of different cells is very similar. Diffusion often takes place across cells. In surfaces that are designed for diffusion, cells will be thin e.g. squamous epithelial.		

WATER POTENTIAL (ψ)

- **Water potential** is a pressure (units: kilopascals kPa).
- It is caused by free water molecules – the more free water molecules, the higher the water potential.

EFFECT OF SOLUTES

- (soluble molecules e.g. glucose) to water: the water molecules stick to the solute and are no longer 'free'. So the water potential falls.

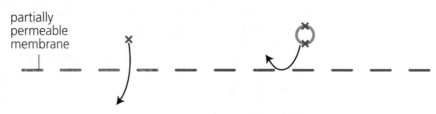

| Free water molecules | Solute | Water molecules attached to solute |

- Only free water can move through a partially permeable membrane.

partially permeable membrane

- Free water diffuses through the membrane in both directions.
- The net effect is that water moves from a region of higher ψ to a region of lower ψ, down a concentration (of water) gradient – by **osmosis**.

OSMOSIS

The highest ψ is that of pure water (all water molecules are free; no solutes).
Its ψ = 0 kPa.
Any **solution** (water plus solute) will have a ψ which is negative.
So a more accurate definition of osmosis is:

- **The movement of water**
- **through a partially permeable membrane**
- **from an area of less negative ψ**
- **to an area of more negative ψ.**

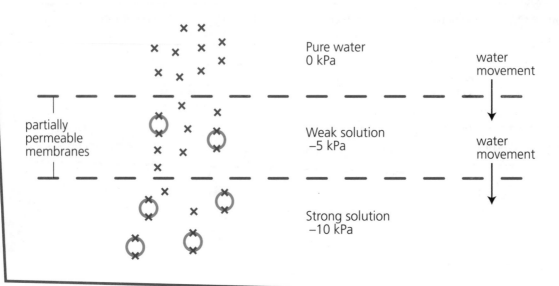

Pure water
0 kPa

water movement

partially permeable membranes

Weak solution
−5 kPa

water movement

Strong solution
−10 kPa

BIOLOGICAL TECHNIQUES

VIEWING AND SEPARATING CELL STRUCTURES

To be able to see organelles, or even biologically important molecules, first magnify them or separate them from one another using one of these techniques:

Technique	Application
Light microscopy	Seeing single objects at least 200 nm across – low resolution – and magnifying them by 1500 times
	A definition of resolution is: **the minimum distance at which two points are distinct.**
Electron microscopy	Producing an image on a film or screen of separate objects that are at least 2 nm across – high resolution – and magnifying them 500 000 times
Cell fractionation	Breaking up cells to release the organelles which can then be separated
Ultracentrifugation	Separating organelles/components of cells by means of their density or mass
Chromatography	Separating molecules by means of their different solubility in solvents and different rates of movement through chromatography paper
Electrophoresis	Separating molecules by means of their charge and the rate at which they move through a gel when exposed to an electric current

MICROSCOPES

Light microscopes use light, so we can:
- see images with our eyes.
- focus using glass lenses.
- see living material.
- use simple stains.

Electron microscopes use electrons, so we must:
- use a screen or photographic film – the eye does not register electrons.
- focus using magnetic lenses.
- use a vacuum, therefore living material cannot be seen.
- use heavy metals as stains (hard to use).

TYPES OF ELECTRON MICROSCOPE

Transmission: Electrons pass through the material, but do not pass through the heavy metal stain – used to see detail of a section.
Scanning: Electrons bounce off stain – used to see 3D views of surfaces.

MUST REMEMBER

The advantage of using the electron microscope is that it has a **better resolution** than a light microscope, due to the **shorter wavelength** of electrons compared with light rays.

CELL FRACTIONATION

Cells are broken open, but to avoid damaging the organelles, certain conditions must be followed.

Experimental detail	Purpose
Suspend the tissue in **isotonic** solution.	The **water potential** of the solution will be the same as that inside the organelles. Water will not move into or leave the organelle, so it will not be damaged.
Add a **buffer** to the solution.	Enzymes are affected by pH and the activity of organelles may in turn be affected if the pH changes. A buffer keeps the **pH constant**.
Surround the solution with **ice**.	Broken lysosomes release their **hydrolytic enzymes** which will digest the organelles. Low temperatures **slow down the activity** of those enzymes.

MUST REMEMBER

Organelles are enclosed in membranes which easily break under pressure.

This solution is now **filtered** to remove clumps of unbroken cells and the **filtrate** containing the organelles is used.

ULTRACENTRIFUGATION

A centrifuge spins the filtrate, forcing organelles down to the bottom of the tube.

The faster the centrifuge spins, the lighter are the organelles which end up at the bottom of the tube.

Speed of centrifuge	Organelles in sediment	Mass
Slow	Nucleus	Light
Fast	Chloroplast	Very light
Very fast	Mitochondria	Very very light
Very very fast	Ribosome	Very very very light

MUST REMEMBER

Will NOT be expected to know the rate at which the centrifuge rotates or the time for the process, but must remember the order in which the organelles are removed from the solution.

CHROMATOGRAPHY

1. Add a solvent to the jar and cover.
2. On a piece of chromatography paper, draw a line in pencil – the **origin**.
3. Using a **micropipette**, put a very small amount of the solution containing a mixture of chemicals onto the origin.
4. Allow to dry.
5. Add another drop – allow to dry.
6. Place the paper in a sealable container. Be sure that the level of the solvent is below the origin.
7. Allow the solvent to travel up the paper, as far as possible.
8. Mark where it stops – the **solvent front**.

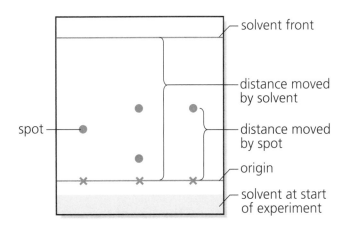

MUST TAKE CARE

Will be expected to have used this technique, so must learn it and be able to explain it.

If spots of the different molecules are not visible, add a stain that allows them to be seen (e.g. amino acids sprayed with **ninhydrin** appear purple).

TWO-WAY CHROMATOGRAPHY

If two molecules are not separated by one solvent:

- Turn the chromatography paper through 90 degrees.
- Run the chromatograph again using a different solvent.

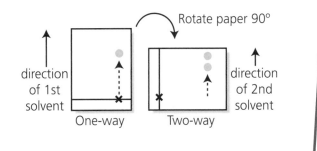

Rf VALUES

Rf values allow substances to be identified.

- As a solvent moves through the paper, molecules are dissolved into the solvent and are carried from the origin.
- The distance moved by a molecule is related to how far the solvent front has moved.
- Comparing these distances produces an **Rf value**:

$$Rf = \frac{\text{Distance the spot moves from the origin}}{\text{Distance the solvent front moves from the origin}}$$

- You always get the same Rf value for a specific substance in a specific solvent.
- To identify the substance, look up this Rf value in a book.

MUST TAKE CARE

Always measure the distance moved by the spot from the origin to the **centre** of the spot.

The Rf value has **no units** and is always **less than 1**.

ELECTROPHORESIS

Electrophoresis is used to separate any charged substance on the basis of its size. The most common is the separation of pieces of DNA. This technique is used in **genetic fingerprinting**.

GENETIC FINGERPRINTING BACKGROUND

- Each DNA molecule has non-coding sections called **introns**.
- Within introns are short sequences of bases which repeat themselves over and over again – up to 100 times. These repeating sequences are called **minisatellites**.
- Cut a piece of DNA and the size of the sections will depend on the number of repeated minisatellites.

Method

1. DNA is digested (broken down) into small pieces using **restriction enzymes**.
2. The pieces of DNA are placed into a well on a gel plate.
3. An electric current is passed from one end of the gel to the other.
4. DNA pieces are negatively charged and will move towards the anode.
5. Small fragments of DNA move further than large fragments.
6. Treat with alkaline solution to break hydrogen bonds and to separate the two strands of DNA.
7. DNA probes are added – short **single strands of DNA** which have complementary bases to the minisatellites and are radioactive or fluorescent.
8. The gel is blotted using a nylon sheet placed on a photographic film.
9. The pattern of bands produced is unique.

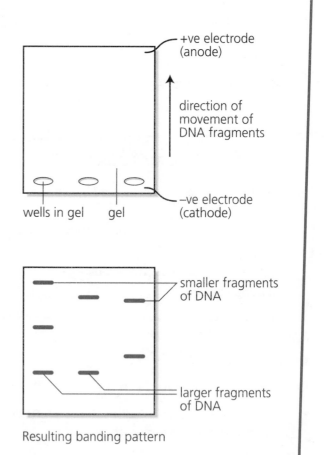

Resulting banding pattern

MUST REMEMBER

- Only identical twins produce the same banding pattern.
- Children have a pattern which contains half the bands of each parent.
- Brothers or sisters have some bands in common.

ENZYMES

ENZYME BASICS

An enzyme is a biological catalyst which speeds up the rate of chemical reactions by lowering the activation energy.

Activation energy is the energy needed to break bonds of the raw materials which starts the reaction.

Energy may be given out by the reaction as heat because:

- The energy of the raw materials is higher than the energy of the products.

This is an **exothermic** reaction.

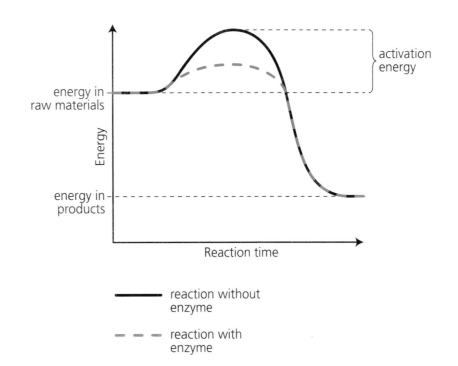

reaction without enzyme

– – – reaction with enzyme

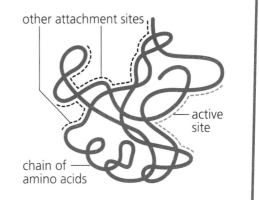

CHARACTERISTICS OF AN ENZYME-CONTROLLED REACTION

- The structure of the enzyme is not altered by the reaction.
- The enzyme is highly specific.

MUST REMEMBER

As the enzyme is not used up by the reaction, only small quantities are needed.

ACTIVE SITE

- All enzymes are tertiary structure proteins and are **globular**.
- The chain of amino acids making up the protein folds and forms cavities.
- Each cavity has a specific shape.
- If the shape of this cavity is **complementary** to another molecule (the **substrate**), that molecule may fit into the active site.
- Here the reaction will take place.

HOW AN ENZYME WORKS

There are two theories:

Theory:	Lock and key	Induced fit
Model	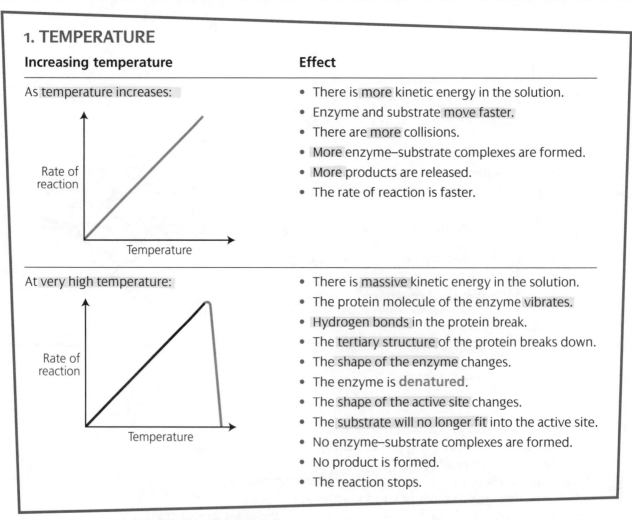 enzyme substrate enzyme–substrate complex	enzyme substrate enzyme–substrate complex
Active site	It is a rigid shape which is **complementary** to the substrate.	It is a flexible shape.
Collisions	If the substrate collides with the active site, it fits exactly.	If the substrate collides with the active site, it enters the active site.
Forming	An **enzyme–substrate complex** is formed.	The active site changes shape to mould itself to the substrate, forming an enzyme-substrate complex.
Reaction	A reaction occurs forming a **product**.	A reaction occurs forming a **product**.
Product	The product is released and the enzyme is ready to receive another substrate.	The product is released and the enzyme's active site changes back to its original shape, ready to receive another substrate.

FACTORS WHICH AFFECT THE RATE OF ENZYME-CONTROLLED REACTIONS

1. TEMPERATURE

Increasing temperature	Effect
As temperature increases: [graph: Rate of reaction vs Temperature, straight increasing line]	<ul><li>There is more kinetic energy in the solution.</li><li>Enzyme and substrate move faster.</li><li>There are more collisions.</li><li>More enzyme–substrate complexes are formed.</li><li>More products are released.</li><li>The rate of reaction is faster.</li></ul>
At very high temperature: [graph: Rate of reaction vs Temperature, line rises then sharply drops]	<ul><li>There is massive kinetic energy in the solution.</li><li>The protein molecule of the enzyme vibrates.</li><li>Hydrogen bonds in the protein break.</li><li>The tertiary structure of the protein breaks down.</li><li>The shape of the enzyme changes.</li><li>The enzyme is denatured.</li><li>The shape of the active site changes.</li><li>The substrate will no longer fit into the active site.</li><li>No enzyme–substrate complexes are formed.</li><li>No product is formed.</li><li>The reaction stops.</li></ul>

MUST REMEMBER

NOT ALL enzymes have an optimum temperature of 40 °C (or body temperature). Must be sure to read the information given in the question or look carefully at the data given in the graph.

2. PH

Changing pH	Effect
At **optimum pH**: 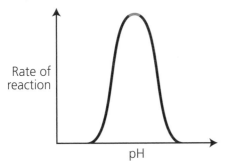	• Correct number of H⁺ are in the solution. • No changes occur to the ionic bonds in the protein. • The tertiary structure of the protein remains. • The shape of the enzyme is unaltered. • Many enzyme–substrate complexes are formed. • Many products are released. • There is the fastest/optimum rate of reaction.
At **lower pH** or at **higher pH**: 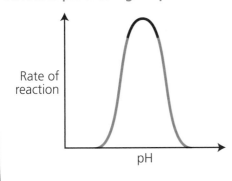	• There is less or more H⁺. • Changes occur to the ionic bonds in the protein. • The tertiary structure of the protein breaks down. • The shape of the enzyme changes. • The shape of the active site changes. • The substrate will no longer fit into the active site. • No enzyme–substrate complexes are formed. • No product is formed. • The reaction stops.

> **MUST REMEMBER**
>
> In a solution there will be millions of enzyme molecules, not all will be affected in the same way at the same time. Therefore some products will be formed over a small range about the optimum pH until all the enzymes are denatured.

3. ENZYME CONCENTRATION

Increasing enzyme concentration	Effect
As **enzyme concentration increases**: 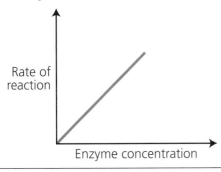	• There are more enzyme molecules, so more active sites are available for the substrate to fit. • More enzyme–substrate complexes are formed. • More products are formed. • The rate of reaction is increased. • The limiting factor is the enzyme concentration.
At **high enzyme concentration**: 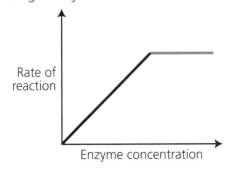	• All the substrate molecules have formed enzyme–substrate complexes. • The enzyme concentration is no longer the limiting factor. • The limiting factor is substrate concentration. (This applies as long as pH and temperature are not limiting factors.)

4. SUBSTRATE CONCENTRATION

Increasing substrate concentration	Effect
As **substrate concentration increases**: 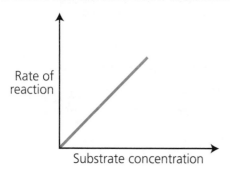	• The more substrate molecules there are, the greater the chance of collision with the enzyme. • With more collisions, more enzyme–substrate complexes are formed. • Rate of reaction increases. • Substrate concentration is limiting.
At **high substrate concentration**: 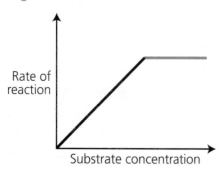	• Increasing the substrate concentration makes no difference to the rate of reaction. • All the enzyme's active sites are occupied. • The enzymes are working at their maximum turnover rate. • The limiting factor is enzyme concentration. (This applies as long as pH and temperature are not limiting factors)

INHIBITORS

Inhibitors slow down the rate of enzyme-controlled reactions.

Inhibitor	Competitive	Non-competitive
Model	active site, substrate, enzyme, competitive inhibitor	non-competitive inhibitor, substrate, enzyme, active site shape changed
Combines with:	• the active site of an enzyme	• another site on the enzyme
Shape is:	• similar to the substrate	• not similar to the substrate
Effect:	• stops the substrate entering the active site • stops enzyme–substrate complex formation	• changes the shape of the enzyme • changes the shape of the active site • stops the substrate entering the active site • stops enzyme–substrate complex formation

MUST TAKE CARE

Never write that the competitive inhibitor is the SAME shape as the substrate.

BLOOD VESSELS

LINKING FEATURES TO ASPECTS OF BLOOD VESSELS

Feature	Artery	Arteriole	Capillary	Vein
Blood flow	Away from the heart to an organ	Within an organ to capillaries	Between cells of an organ	Towards the heart from organs
Oxygen content of blood	High – except the pulmonary artery	High	Oxygen diffuses into tissues	Low – except the pulmonary vein
Blood pressure	High: Blood is forced into arteries from the heart.	Reducing: Blood from one artery will travel in a number of arterioles.	Reducing: Fluid and soluble components of the blood leave the capillary.	Low: Blood enters from the capillaries.
Appearance				

TISSUES IN BLOOD VESSELS

Tissue	Artery	Arteriole	Capillary	Vein	Function
Endothelium (the inner layer made of epithelial cells)	Single layer	Single layer	Single layer	Single layer	It is smooth so that blood cells are not damaged, and allows blood to flow with little friction.
Elastic tissue	Thick layer	Less thick	Not present	Thin layer	It stretches and recoils to smooth out flow of blood.
Muscle tissue	Thick layer	Less thick	Not present	Thin layer	It contracts to reduce the diameter of the vessels, controlling the direction of blood flow. **It is most important in the arterioles.**
Valves	Not present – except in the aorta and pulmonary arteries	Not present	Not present	Present	They stop backflow of blood.

TISSUE FLUID FORMATION

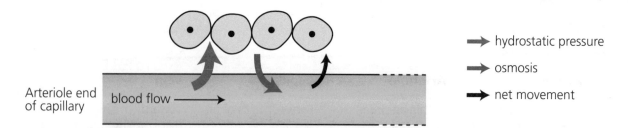

Arteriole end of capillary

blood flow ⟶

→ hydrostatic pressure
→ osmosis
→ net movement

At arteriole end	
• The blood entering the capillary has a high **hydrostatic pressure**. • This forces water AND soluble molecules out of the capillary, forming **tissue fluid**.	• The blood has proteins present which lowers the **water potential**. • The water potential is lower than that surrounding the cells. • Water enters the capillary. • This occurs by **osmosis**.
• Since MORE is pushed out than is returned, • the NET movement of water and soluble molecules is from the capillary to the cells.	

→ hydrostatic pressure
→ osmosis
→ net movement

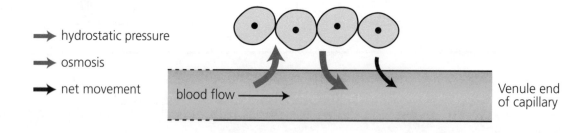

blood flow ⟶

Venule end of capillary

At venule end	
• The proteins do not leave the capillary so the water potential remains low. • The water potential is lower than the fluid surrounding the cells. • Water moves back in to the capillary. • This occurs by **osmosis**.	• The hydrostatic pressure has reduced but it still forces some water and soluble molecules out of the capillaries.
• Since MORE is drawn back into the capillary by the process of osmosis than is being forced out due to the hydrostatic pressure, • the NET movement of water and soluble molecules is back into the capillary.	

MUST TAKE CARE

Must NOT write about plasma leaving the arteriole OR tissue fluid returning to the capillary. It is water and soluble molecules.

MUST REMEMBER

• Proteins are large molecules, so are too large to leave the capillary.
• The hydrostatic pressure is caused by the contraction of the ventricles in the heart.

LYMPH FORMATION

The volume of water and soluble molecules that leaves the capillary is not the same as the volume that returns. Any excess fluid that leaves will enter the lymphatic system and return to the blood at the neck region.

HEART AND CIRCULATION

CIRCULATION

- The pressure to move blood around the body is caused by the contraction of the heart.

- Blood travels around the body in blood vessels (see 'Blood Vessels', pages 19–20).

- The names of some major vessels and those associated with the heart are shown in the diagram.

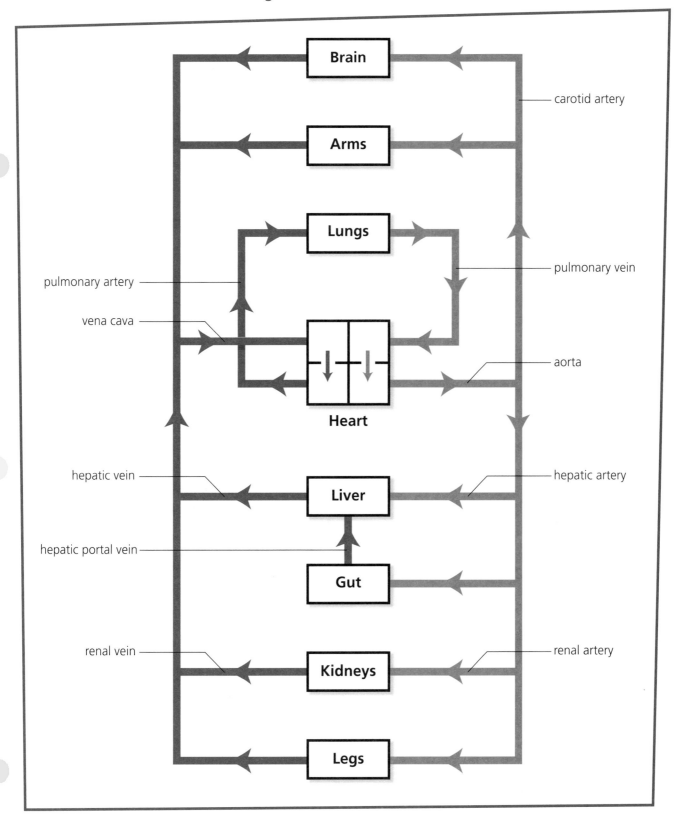

SUMMARY OF HEART STRUCTURE

Features	Diagram

Features

- A pump

- Made of **cardiac muscle**

- Two sides, working at the same time

- **Atria** receive blood from veins. They have **thin** muscular walls.

- **Ventricles** pump blood to body. They have **thick** muscular walls.

- Left ventricle pumps blood to the body. Therefore it has the **thickest** wall.

- Right ventricle pumps blood to **lungs**. Therefore it has a **less thick** wall.

- **Atrioventricular (AV) valves** are between the atria and ventricles.

- **Semilunar valves** are in the **aorta** and **pulmonary artery**.

- Valves prevent backflow of blood.

- Tendons are attached to the atrioventricular valves, preventing the AV valves turning inside out.

Diagram

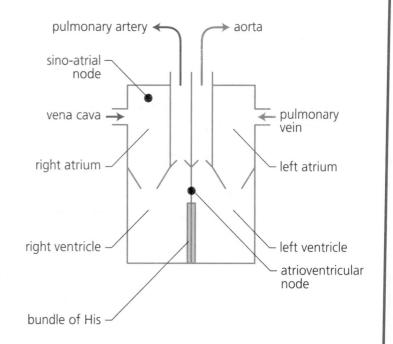

MUST REMEMBER

- Muscle contraction decreases the volume in the heart chambers,
- which increases the pressure,
- which opens and closes valves,
- allowing blood to flow in one direction.

For practice in answering AS Biology questions, why not use *Collins Exam Practice AS Biology*?

THE CARDIAC CYCLE

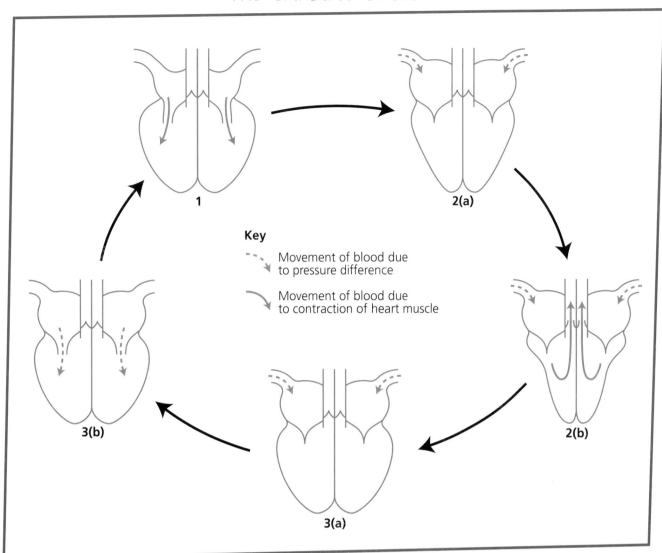

Key

- - → Movement of blood due to pressure difference

⟶ Movement of blood due to contraction of heart muscle

1

2(a)

2(b)

3(a)

3(b)

Stage	Action of atria	Result	Action of ventricles	Result
1. Atrial systole	Walls **contract**.	Blood is forced through atrioventricular valves into ventricles.	Walls relax.	Ventricles fill with blood.
2. Ventricular systole	Walls relax.	Blood enters from the vena cava.	Walls **contract**.	**(a)** No blood leaves but blood pressure in ventricles increases. **(b)** Higher pressure of blood opens semilunar valves and blood is ejected into main arteries.
3. Ventricular diastole	Walls relax.	**(a)** Blood enters atria but cannot pass into ventricles as atrioventricular valves are still closed. **(b)** Valves are now open, so blood enters atria and passes into ventricles.	Walls relax.	**(a)** Higher pressure of blood in arteries closes semilunar valves. Blood neither enters nor leaves. **(b)** Blood enters from atria: passive ventricular filling which is not due to atrial contraction.

PRESSURE AND VOLUME GRAPH OF THE HEART CYCLE

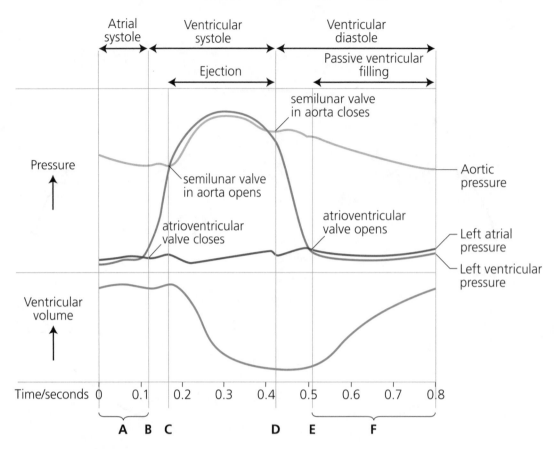

Position	Explanation
A	Atrium is contracting – blood flows into the ventricles.
B	Ventricle starts to contract – **ventricular pressure** exceeds **atrial pressure**, so **atrioventricular valve** closes.
C	**Ventricular pressure** exceeds aortic pressure, forcing **semilunar valve** open. Blood therefore flows from ventricle into aorta and **ventricular volume** falls.
D	**Ventricular pressure** falls below aortic pressure, so **semilunar valve** closes.
E	**Ventricular pressure** falls below **atrial pressure**, so blood flows from atrium to ventricle; **ventricular volume** rises rapidly.
F	Atrium continues to fill with blood from pulmonary vein; **atrial pressure** exceeds ventricular pressure, so blood flows from atrium to ventricle.

MUST TAKE CARE

Often a graph or information given is about one side of the heart, as in this case.

- Make sure to correctly name the vessels associated with that side.
- The other side will be behaving identically.
- If asked to calculate heart rate, note the time the cycle starts to repeat itself: 0.8 seconds for one cycle.
- Therefore in one minute it will be $\frac{60}{0.8}$ = 75 beats per minute.

CONTROL OF HEART BEAT

- Origin of heart beat is in the heart muscle itself.
- It is called **myogenic** stimulation.
- A wave of contraction then spreads through heart, allowing all the heart to beat at the same rate.

What happens – step by step	Diagram

1. Sino-atrial node (SAN) produces an impulse,

- **which spreads over the atria causing the muscle to contract.**
- **Impulses reach atrioventricular node (AVN).**

2. Impulses cannot cross directly into ventricles due to a plate of fibrous tissue. The impulse passes through the AVN slowly, causing a delay, to allow complete contraction of the atria.

- **Impulse passes into specialised fibres called the bundle of His.**
- **The impulse is carried to the apex of heart** BUT
- does not cause the muscle of the ventricles to contract.

- **Impulse spreads back towards the atria,**
- **causing ventricle muscle to contract.**
- This ensures the ventricles contract from apex to atria – pushing blood up towards the arteries.

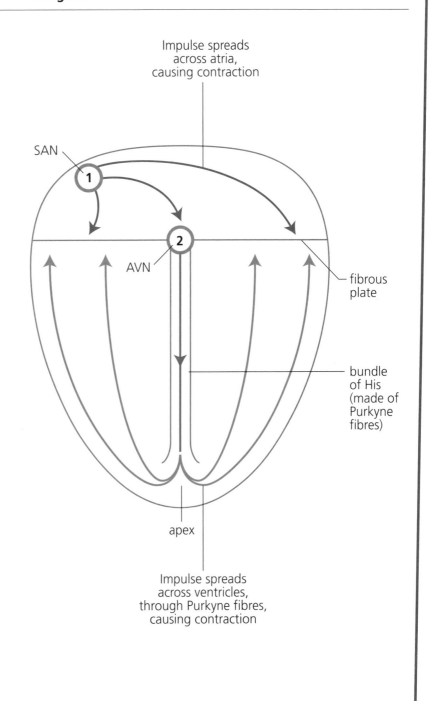

Impulse spreads across atria, causing contraction

SAN

1

AVN

2

fibrous plate

bundle of His (made of Purkyne fibres)

apex

Impulse spreads across ventricles, through Purkyne fibres, causing contraction

CHANGING HEART RATE

Though the stimulus for the heart beat is myogenic, to change the rate at which the heart beats, an outside stimulus is required.

This stimulus is from either the nervous system or hormones.

Nervous control	Diagram
To speed up heart rate: • more impulses are sent down the **accelerator** nerve • to the **SAN** • which sends more impulses through the heart. To slow down heart rate: • more impulses are sent down the **vagus** nerve • to the **SAN** • which sends fewer impulses through the heart. **Hormonal control** To speed up heart rate: • **adrenaline** is released • It travels in the blood to the **SAN**. • It stimulates the SAN to send more impulses through the heart.	

MUST REMEMBER

• The accelerator nerve speeds up the heart beat.
• The vagus nerve slows down the heart beat.

MUST TAKE CARE

• Must NEVER use the terms 'signals' or 'messages'; always refer to 'impulses'.
• Must always write 'MORE impulses' will cause change. It is not enough to identify the nerve carrying the impulse.

THE LUNGS AND VENTILATION

SIZE AND ITS EFFECT ON SURFACE AREA : VOLUME RATIO

- All organisms, big or small, that respire aerobically require oxygen.

- The efficiency of diffusion depends on the **surface area : volume ratio**, so very small organisms can meet all their gas exchange needs by diffusion through their surface.

- Larger organisms require specialised gas exchange systems that increase the surface area over which diffusion can take place.

> **MUST TAKE CARE**
>
> Breathing is **not** the same as respiration.
>
> Aerobic respiration:
> - is the complete breakdown of the chemicals we eat.
> - produces the maximum amount of ATP.
> - involves OXYGEN.

Small organisms:
Because they have a large surface area when compared with their volume, they take in oxygen by **diffusion** through their body surface.

Large organisms:
Because they have a small surface area : volume ratio, they have a respiratory surface, such as a **lung**.

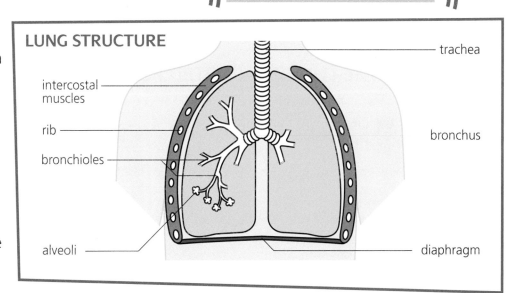

LUNG STRUCTURE

trachea, intercostal muscles, rib, bronchioles, alveoli, bronchus, diaphragm

VENTILATION

- **Ventilation** is the mechanism by which air is brought into the lungs and removed from them.

- Oxygen is taken up across all gas exchange surfaces by diffusion.

- A ventilation mechanism ensures that the difference in concentration across such a surface is kept as high as possible.

Process	Muscle action	What happens
Inhalation/ breathing in	Diaphragm muscle **contracts**.	Diaphragm **flattens**.
	External intercostal muscles **contract**.	Ribs move **up and out**.
		• Volume in thorax increases. • Pressure in thorax decreases. • Air moves down a pressure gradient and into the lungs.
Exhalation/ breathing out	Diaphragm muscle **relaxes**.	Diaphragm becomes **dome shaped**.
	External intercostal muscles **relax**.	Ribs move down and in: • Volume in thorax decreases. • Pressure in thorax increases. • Air moves down a pressure gradient and out of the lungs.

GAS EXCHANGE

- Oxygen enters the blood from the air spaces of the alveoli, and is exchanged for carbon dioxide.

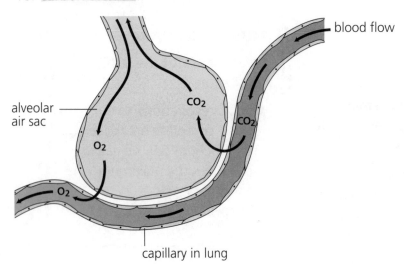

blood flow

alveolar air sac

CO₂

CO₂

O₂

O₂

capillary in lung

MUST TAKE CARE

Oxygen and carbon dioxide are transported by the process of diffusion.

Efficient diffusion relies on the principles found in Fick's law, page 9.

Refer to 'Biological molecules', pages 1–4, and review Fick's law.

THE LUNG IS ADAPTED FOR GAS EXCHANGE

How does the lung make gas exchange efficient?	Feature
There is a large surface area.	• The lung has many alveoli. – The surface area is greater in a group of alveoli than in a same-size simple air sac. Simple air sac Many alveoli
There is a large diffusion gradient.	• Breathing air delivers oxygen to the alveoli – high concentration. O_2 high O_2 concentration low O_2 concentration • Circulating blood removes oxygen – low concentration.
There is a short distance to travel.	• The distance that oxygen has to travel is very short, • made possible by having only two cells to cross, both of which are modified to be extremely thin, **squamous cells**. short distance

MUST REMEMBER

Gas exchange only takes place in the alveoli.

Other parts of the system will therefore have different concentrations of oxygen and carbon dioxide from that found in the alveoli.

For example, the trachea will have:

- a higher concentration of oxygen than the alveoli.
- a lower concentration of carbon dioxide than the alveoli.

CONTROL OF VENTILATION

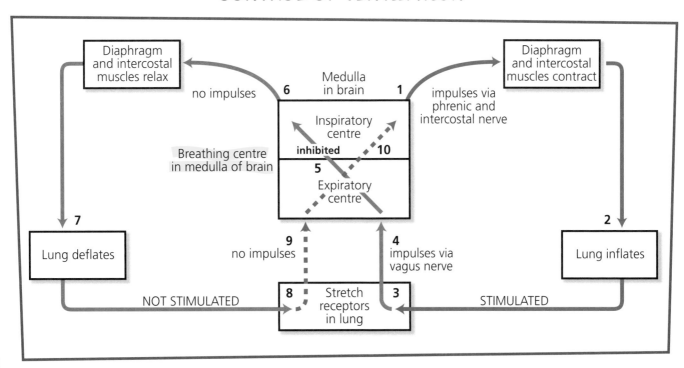

Breathing is a continuous process and is controlled by the **medulla** in the brain.

1. The **inspiratory centre** sends out impulses to the diaphragm and intercostal muscles.
2. This results in inhalation and thus the lungs inflate.
3. Inflation of the lungs is detected by **stretch receptors** in the lungs.
4. These receptors send impulses to the **expiratory centre**.
5. The expiratory centre inhibits the inspiratory centre.
6. The inspiratory centre stops sending impulses to the diaphragm and the intercostal muscles, and they relax ...
7. resulting in exhalation, and the lungs deflate.
8. The deflation is detected by stretch receptors in the lungs.
9. No impulses are sent to the expiratory centre.
10. There is no inhibition of the inspiratory centre.

The cycle is repeated ...

CHANGING BREATHING RATE

In several circumstances, the breathing rate will change, e.g. during exercise and sleeping.
The rate is mainly controlled by the levels of carbon dioxide in the blood.

Increasing breathing rate	Decreasing breathing rate
• Greater activity requires more energy.	• Less activity requires less energy.
• More ATP is produced by increased respiration.	• Less ATP is produced by decreased respiration.
• Increased respiration will produce more carbon dioxide.	• Decreased respiration will produce less carbon dioxide.
• The high levels are detected by receptors in the **carotid body** and **aortic body** and by the **medulla** itself.	• The low levels are detected by receptors in the carotid body and aortic body and by the medulla itself.
• These send **MORE** impulses to the breathing centre.	• These send **FEWER** impulses to the breathing centre.
• The inspiratory centre will respond by sending **MORE** impulses which results in an increase in breathing rate.	• The inspiratory centre will respond by sending **FEWER** impulses, which results in a decrease in breathing rate.

THE CELL CYCLE AND MITOSIS

The **cell cycle** represents the stages of the life cycle of a cell.

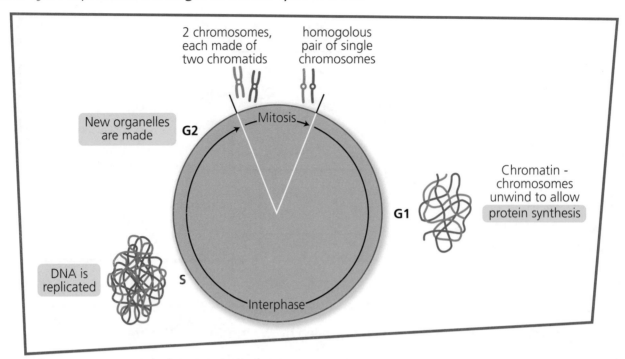

Interphase		This is the stage when the cell is growing.
G1		• Chromosomes unwind: the material formed is called **chromatin**. • Enzymes can come in contact with the DNA. • **Protein synthesis** occurs.
S		• DNA is **replicated**.
G2		• New organelles are formed.
Mitosis		**This is the stage when the nucleus divides.**
Prophase		• Chromatin becomes shorter and fatter, forming distinct visible **chromosomes**. • Chromosomes are double structures made of two identical **chromatids** joined by a **centromere**. • Nuclear envelope breaks down.
Metaphase		• The chromosomes arrange themselves on the **equator** (middle) of the cell. • Spindle fibres are formed by **centrioles**. • Spindle fibres attach to the centromere of each chromosome.
Anaphase	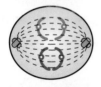	• Spindle fibres shorten. • Centromere of each chromosome splits. • Chromatids are separated. • Chromosomes move apart, towards the poles of the cell.
Telophase		Chromosomes reach the poles of the cell. A new nuclear envelope forms around each of the two sets of chromosomes.
Cytokinesis		**This is when the cytoplasm of the cell splits in two.**
		• Two new cells are formed.

DNA AND RNA

COMPARING DNA AND RNA

DNA	RNA
It is a **polymer**. The monomers are **DNA nucleotides**.	It is a **polymer**. The monomers are **RNA nucleotides**.
Each nucleotide made of: • Phosphate • **Deoxyribose sugar** • Nitrogenous base	Each nucleotide made of: • Phosphate • **Ribose sugar** • Nitrogenous base
Together they form:	Together they form:

Four different nitrogenous bases are put into two groups:
 	
1. Pyrimidines (small molecules)
 	
  • adenine
 	
  • guanine
 	
2. Purines (large molecules)
 	
  • **thymine**
 	
  • cytosine
	Four different nitrogenous bases are put into two groups:
	
	1. Pyrimidines (small molecules)
	
	  • adenine
	
	  • guanine
	
	2. Purines (large molecules)
	
	  • **uracil**
	
	  • cytosine

The **DNA nucleotides** are then joined together by strong covalent bonds forming a long strand.	The **RNA nucleotides** are then joined together by strong covalent bonds forming a short strand.
Two strands are joined together by their bases:	Single strand only

(continued)

COMPARING DNA AND RNA

DNA	RNA	
Strands are linked by **complementary** bases • adenine–thymine, joined by two hydrogen bonds • cytosine–guanine, joined by three hydrogen bonds		
Only found in nucleus	Found in nucleus or cytoplasm	
Only one form	More than one form: • messenger – **mRNA** • transfer – **tRNA**	
	mRNA	**tRNA**
Long lasting – exists for the life of the cell, contains a code enabling the cell to produce any type of protein	Short life – broken down when it has been used to produce a limited number of molecules of a type of protein	Long lasting – is recycled once it has delivered a specific type of amino acid to a forming protein (see Translation, page 37)
Many base pairs form the double helix: 	No base pairs – a single strand: 	Some base pairs – some sections of the single strand are linked forming a clover leaf shape:

For practice in answering AS Biology questions, why not use *Collins Exam Practice AS Biology*?

DNA REPLICATION

The process of DNA replication is called **semi-conservative replication**.

1. Original length of DNA:

$$\left|\begin{array}{l}A=T\\T=A\\C\equiv G\\G\equiv C\end{array}\right|$$

2. • DNA strands unwind.
   • Hydrogen bonds between the strands break.

$$\left|\begin{array}{ll}A&T\\T&A\\C&G\\G&C\end{array}\right|$$

3. Complementary bases separate and the two strands separate.

$$\left|\begin{array}{l}A\\T\\C\\G\end{array}\right.\qquad\left.\begin{array}{l}T\\A\\G\\C\end{array}\right|$$

4. • Free DNA nucleotides are present in the nucleus.
   • Complementary DNA nucleotides with complementary bases associate with both strands.

$$\left|\begin{array}{l}A=T\,|\\T=A|\\C\equiv G|\\G\equiv C|\end{array}\right.\qquad\left|\begin{array}{l}A=T\\T=A\\C\equiv G\\G\equiv C\end{array}\right|$$

5. **DNA polymerase** links the sugar/phosphate backbones.

$$\left|\begin{array}{l}A=T\\T=A\\C\equiv G\\G\equiv C\end{array}\right|\qquad\begin{array}{l}\text{DNA}\\\text{polymerase}\end{array}\qquad\left|\begin{array}{l}A=T\\T=A\\C\equiv G\\G\equiv C\end{array}\right|$$

6. Two identical lengths of DNA are produced.

$$\left|\begin{array}{l}A=T\\T=A\\C\equiv G\\G\equiv C\end{array}\right|\qquad\left|\begin{array}{l}A=T\\T=A\\C\equiv G\\G\equiv C\end{array}\right|$$

Meselsohn and Stahl proved experimentally that DNA replication was semi-conservative.

- Bacteria were grown on a medium containing the heavy isotope of nitrogen, ^{15}N.

- The nitrogen was made into nitrogenous bases in both strands of their DNA.

- A sample of bacteria was fractionated and centrifuged, and their DNA settled (see tube **A**).

- The remaining bacteria were then grown on a medium containing the light (normal) isotope of nitrogen, ^{14}N.

- After **one generation** the bacteria were fractionated and centrifuged, and their DNA settled (see tube **B**).

- After **two generations** the bacteria were fractionated and centrifuged, and their DNA settled (see tube **C**).

- The results support the semi-conservative replication theory.

Original bacteria (tube A)
All the bacteria contained ^{15}N in both their strands of DNA.

Result – heavy weight DNA

First generation (tube B)
All the DNA is made from:
- one strand of the original heavy ^{15}N nucleotides, **and**
- one new light strand of ^{14}N nucleotides

Result – medium weight DNA

Second generation (tube C)
Half the bacteria will contain DNA that is made from:
- one strand of the original heavy ^{15}N nucleotides, **and**
- one new light strand of ^{14}N nucleotides

Result – medium weight DNA

The other half of the bacteria will contain DNA that is made from:
- one new light strand of ^{14}N nucleotides, **and**
- one new light strand of ^{14}N nucleotides

Result – light weight DNA

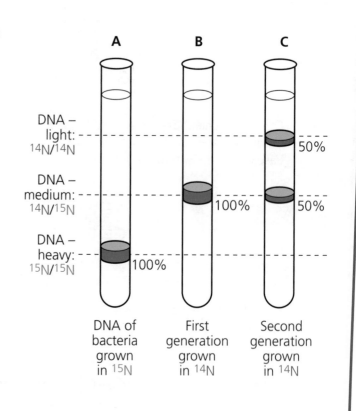

DNA – light: ^{14}N/^{14}N

DNA – medium: ^{14}N/^{15}N

DNA – heavy: ^{15}N/^{15}N

A — 100%

B — 100%

C — 50% / 50%

DNA of bacteria grown in ^{15}N

First generation grown in ^{14}N

Second generation grown in ^{14}N

PROTEIN SYNTHESIS

- DNA is divided into sections called **genes**.
- Each gene is a specific length of DNA.
- Its sequence of nucleotide bases codes for a specific order of amino acids.
- A specific sequence of amino acids forms a particular polypeptide or protein.

Code property	Explanation
triplet code	A sequence of **three DNA bases** codes for each amino acid.
non-overlapping code	Each set of three bases is read once, like a frame of a film. Once read in one frame, a base is not read again in the next.
degenerate code	More than one triplet code can code for the same amino acid.
universal code	One triplet of bases codes for the same amino acid for all organisms in which the DNA is found.

Protein synthesis consists of two stages:

- **Transcription** of DNA – in nucleus
- **Translation** of mRNA – in ribosomes in the cytoplasm

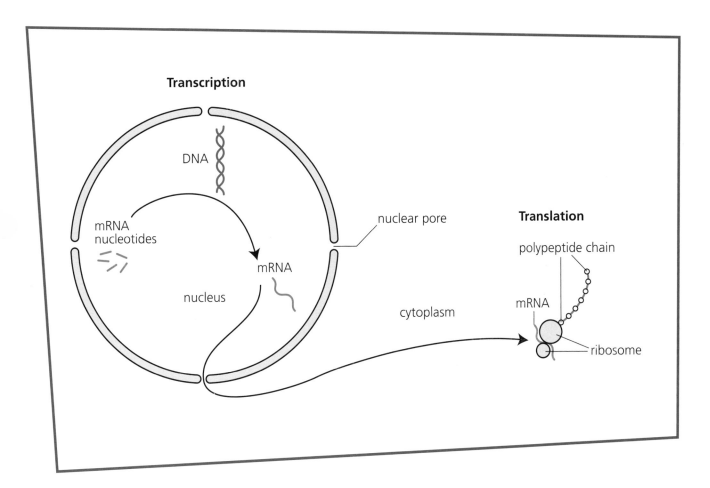

TRANSCRIPTION

MAKING mRNA USING DNA AS A TEMPLATE

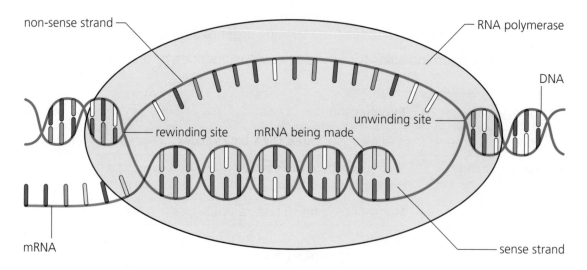

What happens	More detail
Section of DNA that codes for a protein unwinds.	Only a small section that codes for the protein will unwind at a time.
Hydrogen bonds between complementary bases break.	These are the weak bonds in the DNA molecule and an enzyme breaks them.
Complementary **RNA nucleotides** line up against the **sense strand** of the DNA.	DNA RNA thymine............adenine adenine.............uracil guanine............cytosine cytosine............guanine

- **RNA polymerase** joins sugar and phosphate of adjacent RNA nucleotides.
- Single strand of mRNA is formed ...
- ... made of bases complementary to the triplets of bases in DNA.
- mRNA leaves the nucleus ...
- ... through a nuclear pore.

mRNA is a mobile copy of a gene.
Each set of three bases in mRNA is called a **codon**.

MUST TAKE CARE

mRNA is very different from DNA:

- You cannot **make** one from the other because they are made of a different pentose sugar, and one of the four bases is also different.

- mRNA transcription is NOT the same as DNA replication, even though it has similarities. For example, in transcription, RNA polymerase is the enzyme involved, whereas in replication it is DNA polymerase.

tRNA ACTIVATION

- Each molecule of **tRNA** links with a specific amino acid.
- The amino acid that joins to a tRNA molecule is determined by a set of three bases called the **anticodon**.
- Each anticodon is complementary to one mRNA codon.

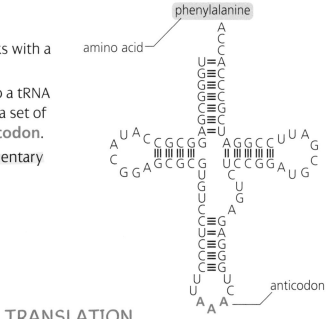

TRANSLATION

MAKING A POLYPEPTIDE USING A mRNA TEMPLATE

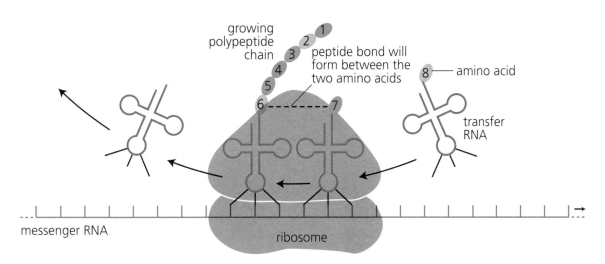

What happens	More detail
• A mRNA strand enters a ribosome. • The first set of three bases (codon) is read.	The first codon is always AUG. It is the **'Start' code**.
• A codon of mRNA links with the anticodon of a specific tRNA.	**AUG** of mRNA links with **UAC** of tRNA.
• An amino acid specific to this tRNA is brought into the ribosome.	In this case the amino acid is methionine.
• The second codon of mRNA is read. • This codon links with an anticodon of a specific tRNA. • Another specific amino acid is brought into the ribosome. • This amino acid is joined to the first by a **peptide bond**.	
• The third codon is read … and so on. • The amino acids form a **polypeptide chain**.	

FROM DNA TO AN AMINO ACID SEQUENCE

In the example below:

- Four sets of DNA base triplets are transcribed into a mRNA strand containing 4 codons.

- Four different tRNA molecules, each containing a complementary anticodon, provide specific amino acids during translation, or code for Stop.

- Note: There is one code for Start and more than one for Stop.

DNA triplet →	mRNA codon →	tRNA anticodon →	Amino acid
T	A	U	Start
A	U	A	methionine
C	G	C	
G	C	G	glycine
T	A	U	
T	A	U	
A	U	A	serine
G	C	G	
A	U	A	
A	U	A	Stop
C	G	C	
T	A	U	

MUST REMEMBER

- A sequence of amino acids forms a polypeptide. This is not a protein (see 'Biological molecules', page 2).

- Methionine is always the first amino acid to start the sequence.

- It is often removed, not forming part of the polypeptide chain.

- Need not remember any of the codes for specific amino acids as they will always be provided when necessary.

For practice in answering AS Biology questions, why not use *Collins Exam Practice AS Biology*?

GENETIC ENGINEERING

Genetic engineering is possible because DNA has a **universal code**.
All organisms read the nucleotide sequence of a **particular triplet code** as the **same amino acid**.

RECOMBINANT DNA TECHNOLOGY

- This involves combining DNA from one organism with DNA from another organism.
- The inserted DNA is read by the new cell, and the protein for which it codes is produced.
- We are able to use different ways to produce recombinant DNA.
- The method used depends on the organism the DNA is extracted from, and the organism it is put into.

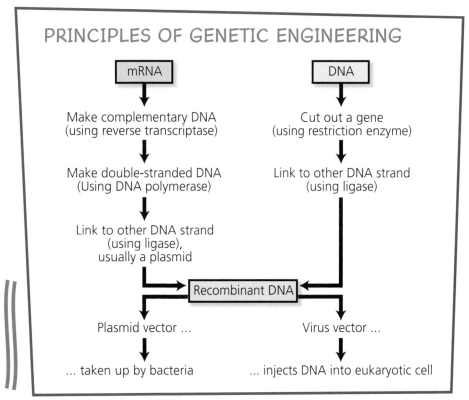

PRINCIPLES OF GENETIC ENGINEERING

mRNA

Make complementary DNA
(using reverse transcriptase)

Make double-stranded DNA
(Using DNA polymerase)

Link to other DNA strand
(using ligase),
usually a plasmid

DNA

Cut out a gene
(using restriction enzyme)

Link to other DNA strand
(using ligase)

Recombinant DNA

Plasmid vector ...

... taken up by bacteria

Virus vector ...

... injects DNA into eukaryotic cell

MUST REMEMBER

Viruses can be used as vectors to introduce recombinant DNA into animal or plant cells.

A. STARTING WITH DNA

1. The DNA/gene is isolated.

Segment of DNA removed ...

... and linked with plasmid

Restriction enzymes act only on **specific base sequences** of DNA. Some produce **staggered cuts** across the DNA and therefore a section of unpaired bases – **'sticky ends'**.

By choosing the 'right' restriction enzyme, a gene can be chopped out of the DNA without destroying it. For example, the sequence of bases being cut could be:

G A A T T C
C T T A A G

Make sure this sequence is not in the required gene. If it is, another restriction enzyme must be used.

2. The gene is incorporated into a vector – usually a **plasmid** from a bacterium – forming a **recombinant plasmid**.

The DNA of the plasmid is cut using the same restriction enzyme. It is then joined with the cut-out gene. As they now have complementary sticky ends they will join together. **Ligase** enzyme is used to join the sugar–phosphate backbones.

3. The plasmid is put into a bacterium.

Once inside, the bacterium will read the 'new' genetic code in the plasmid and produce the appropriate protein.

B. STARTING WITH mRNA

Specific method: Insulin production

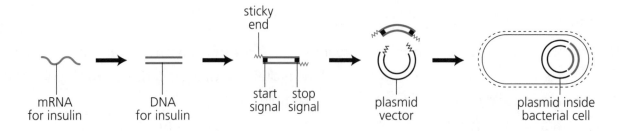

| mRNA for insulin | DNA for insulin | start signal / stop signal (sticky end) | plasmid vector | plasmid inside bacterial cell |

Method	More detail
Isolate **mRNA** that codes for insulin.	Eukaryotic DNA contains **introns**; bacterial DNA does not. Bacterial cells have no method of removing introns. So we start with mRNA that is intron-free rather than DNA.
The enzyme **reverse transcriptase** is used to generate **cDNA**.	**cDNA** is a single strand of DNA, **complementary** to the mRNA.
The cDNA is copied to form double-stranded DNA.	A double strand is required so that it can join with the DNA of the bacterium which is double stranded.
'Start' and 'Stop' signals are added, together with **sticky ends**.	During protein synthesis the signals indicate where the gene begins and ends. The sticky ends allow the gene to join with the bacterial DNA.
The gene is inserted into a **plasmid**, forming **recombinant DNA** using the enzyme **ligase**.	The **plasmid** must be cut with a **restriction enzyme** that gives sticky ends that are **complementary** to the ones added to the gene.
The 'recombinant' plasmid is then put into the bacterium.	The bacterial culture is often mixed with a **cold calcium chloride** solution to make the bacterial membrane more permeable and readily take up the plasmid.
Finally, the bacterium is cloned and then cultured.	• Cloning allows many bacteria to have an identical copy of the recombinant DNA. • Culturing allows the insulin produced to be extracted and purified.

BIOTECHNOLOGY

APPLICATIONS OF ENZYMES

USE OF ENZYMES IN INDUSTRY

Property of enzymes	Advantage
Specific and will only respond to a particular substance	Used to indicate the presence of specific chemicals – e.g. glucose in blood
Very sensitive	Used to measure tiny concentrations of substances
Speed up the rate of reaction but function at low temperatures and mild conditions	No need for expensive equipment, high temperatures or high pressures
Do not change the end product	No by-products to remove as there is no contamination of the product
So the process will be cheaper.	

Problem

• Although enzymes are not used up in a reaction, separation of enzyme from product is expensive and time consuming.

• So enzymes used in industry are often **immobilised**.

Solution: Immobilised enzymes

Immobilised enzyme	Advantages
Definition: **An enzyme that is attached to an insoluble or inert material which holds the enzyme in place during a reaction.** enzyme molecule microcapsule such as an alginate bead	• The enzyme can be reused. • Enzyme does not contaminate the product. • Enzyme does not degrade when temperature rises, so can withstand high temperatures (**thermostable**). • Enzyme structure is more stable due to bonds with the insoluble material, so can withstand extremes of pH.

ISOLATION OF ENZYMES

Enzymes produced by cells can be

- either passed out of the cell – extracellular
- or used within the cell – **intracellular**.

Extracellular enzymes can be separated from cells within a fermenter, but to isolate intracellular enzymes the cells must first be broken down, which makes separation more difficult.

The production of pure enzyme is known as **downstream processing**.

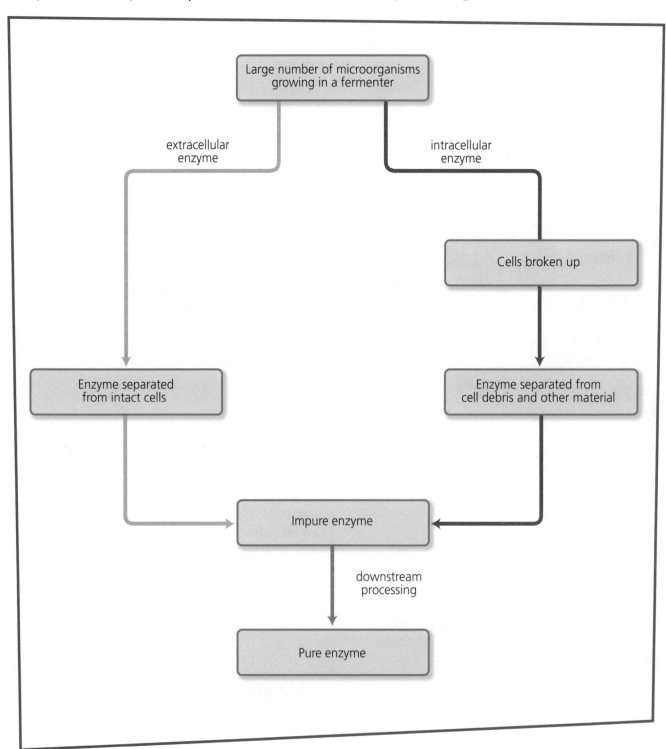

GENE TECHNOLOGY

GENETIC FINGERPRINTING

See 'Electrophoresis' on page 14 for background to the process.

Stage	Detail	Extension
1. Extraction	DNA is extracted from a sample of cells.	Any cell containing a nucleus, e.g. drop of blood, semen or hair root
2. Digestion	DNA is cut using **restriction enzymes**.	These enzymes cut the DNA either side of the repeated **minisatellite**, and provide DNA fragments of different lengths, some containing the minisatellite.
3. Separation	DNA fragments are separated according to size by **electrophoresis**.	Small fragments travel further than large ones.
4. Hybridisation	DNA fragments are transferred onto a nylon membrane, covered in a solution containing a **DNA probe**.	The DNA probe binds to the complementary **core repeating sequences**, making them visible.

POLYMERASE CHAIN REACTION OR PCR

It can be difficult to obtain large quantities of DNA. This technique:

- is used to increase the amount of DNA present.
- involves repeated **DNA replication**.

DETAIL OF PCR

Stage	What is happening
1	DNA is heated to 95 °C. This breaks the hydrogen bonds in the double strand to make it single-stranded DNA.

```
                                        AATCGTATGCTATTA
        AATCGTATGCTATTA
        TTAGCATACGATAAT
                                        TTAGCATACGATAAT
```

| 2 | Add reaction mixture:
• DNA polymerase (enzyme)
• DNA nucleotides with bases A, T, C and G
• and excess **DNA primers**
DNA polymerase cannot work on a single-stranded template. Therefore DNA primers are used.
DNA primers are short single-stranded lengths of DNA, complementary to a few bases at the ends of the DNA strands. |

(continued)

DETAIL OF PCR continued

Stage	What is happening
3	DNA primers (shown as **AAT** here) join to DNA at one end:

A A T C G T A T G C T A T T A

                     A A T

A A T

T T A G C A T A C G A T A A T

Stage	What is happening
4	DNA polymerase joins complementary bases to each single DNA strand, producing two double strands which are identical:

A A T C G T A T G C T A T T A
T T A G C A T A C G A T **A A T**

A A T C G T A T G C T A T T A
T T A G C A T A C G A T A A T

SUMMARY OF PCR

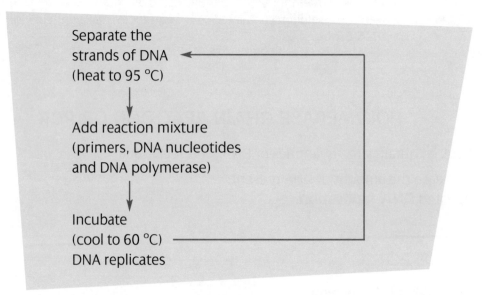

Separate the strands of DNA (heat to 95 °C)

↓

Add reaction mixture (primers, DNA nucleotides and DNA polymerase)

↓

Incubate (cool to 60 °C)
DNA replicates

The number of extra strands of DNA increases slowly at first, but after a few cycles millions of DNA molecules can be produced from a single strand.

It is now possible to use this material for genetic fingerprinting.

PCR cycles	No. of DNA strands
1	2
2	4
3	8
4	16
5	32
10	1024
15	32 768
20	1 048 576
25	33 554 432

BLOOD AND BLOOD CELLS

Blood is a tissue composed of plasma and cells.

PLASMA

- Plasma is the liquid part of the blood.
- It transports soluble substances around the body, e.g. glucose, amino acids, hormones and minerals.
- It supplies and receives substances from body cells, and the amount of each substance in the plasma may vary.

There are several different blood components, but it is necessary to remember just four: red blood cells and three types of white blood cell.

RED BLOOD CELLS

Diagram	Feature of cell	Function
	Shape A disc, indented on both faces	Large surface area : volume ratio for rapid diffusion of oxygen and carbon dioxide
	Nucleus None present	Large internal volume, to hold the maximum volume of haemoglobin
	Other organelles None present	
	Haemoglobin A red pigment	Combines with oxygen to form oxyhaemoglobin, very readily when there is a high oxygen concentration, e.g. in the lungs Haemoglobin also carries some carbon dioxide. Most carbon dioxide is carried in the plasma of the blood as hydrogencarbonate ions.

MUST TAKE CARE

- A group of the same type of cells that carry out the same function is called a **tissue**.
- Other examples include: epithelial tissue, connective tissue and muscle.
- A group of several tissues fulfilling a function is call an **organ**.
- Examples of organs include obvious structures like the heart, lungs, liver; but less obvious things like arteries and veins.

WHITE BLOOD CELLS

Must recognise three different types of white blood cell.
They all have these features in common:

- None contains haemoglobin, so they are not red.
- All have a nucleus.

Diagram	Feature of cell	Function
Granulocyte	• Cytoplasm is granular. • Nucleus is lobed.	• It engulfs bacteria (by phagocytosis). • It is involved in the allergic response.
Lymphocyte	• Cytoplasm is not granular. • Nucleus is round, large and fills up almost all of the cell.	• It produces antibodies. • It is involved in the humoral immune response.
Monocyte	• Cytoplasm is not granular. • Nucleus is a kidney bean shape.	• It engulfs bacteria (by phagocytosis).

For practice in answering
AS Biology questions,
why not use *Collins Exam
Practice AS Biology*?

EFFECT OF EXERCISE

EFFECT OF EXERCISE ON THE HEART

Exercise increases **cardiac output** by increasing both **stroke volume** and **heart rate**.

Cardiac output = stroke volume × heart rate

That is, cardiac output = the amount of blood passing out of the heart per cardiac cycle

multiplied by

how many times the heart beats per minute

No exercise/sleeping	Little exercise/sitting	Heavy exercise/running
Slower heart beat	Normal heart beat	Faster heart beat
More impulses from the **vagus nerve**	**Myogenic** control (see 'Heart and circulation', pages 21–26)	More impulses from the **accelerator nerve** Hormone effect – adrenaline
Imagine a car – **running downhill with the driver's foot on the break.**	Imagine a car – **freewheeling downhill.**	Imagine a car – **running downhill with the driver's foot on the accelerator.**

EFFECT OF EXERCISE ON THE DISTRIBUTION OF BLOOD

The amount of blood going to different organs varies when doing exercise.
This is due to:

- **vasoconstriction** – the muscles in the arterioles contract and reduce the flow of blood
- **vasodilation** – the muscles in the arterioles relax and increase the flow of blood

BLOOD SUPPLY TO ORGANS DURING EXERCISE

Increases to...	Constant to...	Decreases to...
Muscle • providing more oxygen and nutrients Skin • which removes excess heat by convection	Brain • still requires nutrients and oxygen to function when the body is under stress	Gut • digesting and absorbing nutrients is not a priority Kidney • removing waste from the blood is not a priority

EFFECT OF EXERCISE ON VENTILATION

Ventilation is controlled by the medulla (see 'The lungs and ventilation', pages 27–29) and both rate and depth of breathing are increased during exercise, with changing carbon dioxide levels in the blood.

Terms given to volumes of air in the lungs	What the terms means
Vital capacity	The **maximum** amount of air that can be exhaled, after a deep in-breath The **maximum** usable volume of the lungs **This will increase with exercise.**
Residual volume	The **air left** in the lungs after full exhalation This stops the sides of the lungs coming together. **This is still unused, even with strenuous exercise.**
Tidal volume	The volume of air taken into the lungs during a **normal breath** ... ... when the body is at rest **This will get larger and faster with exercise.**
Inspiratory reserve	The **extra** volume of air that can be **forced into** the lungs **This will get larger with exercise.**
Expiratory reserve	The **extra** volume of air that can be **forced out of** the lungs **This will get larger with exercise.**

A trace on a **spirometer** shows the different breathing patterns:

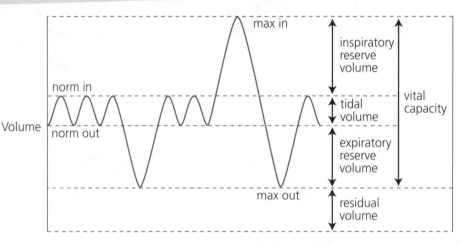

EFFECT ON INHALATION AND EXHALATION

Breathing	Inhalation	Exhalation
At rest	External intercostal muscles contract: • ribs **pulled** up and out	External intercostal muscles relax: • ribs move down and in, due to recoil of rib cage
During exercise	External intercostal muscles contract: • ribs **pulled** up and out	Internal intercostal muscles relax: • ribs move down and in, due to recoil of rib cage Internal intercostal muscles contract: • ribs **pulled** down and in **Therefore, as exhalation is faster, the next breath starts earlier.**

MUST TAKE CARE

At rest the ribs are **not** moved down by the contraction of the internal intercostal muscles.

Movement down happens passively when the cartilage in the rib cage recoils as the external intercostal muscles are relaxed. The internal intercostal muscles are used only in exercise.

IMMUNOLOGY

ANTIGENS

Antigens are:

- molecules that trigger an immune response.
- usually **proteins** but could be polysaccharides, lipids or nucleic acids.

SELF AND NON-SELF ANTIGENS

Self antigen	Non-self antigen
Molecule on our own cell to which we do not respond, but other organisms may.	Molecule on a cell entering the body to which our cells respond. Non-self antigens produce an immune response in the body.

ANTIBODIES

An antibody is always a protein.

- An **antibody** is produced by a specific white blood cell, a **B-lymphocyte** (in response to a non-self antigen).

- An antibody is *not* 'a body'.
- An antibody acts against an antigen.

STAGES OF RESPONSE TO A NON-SELF ANTIGEN

Ingestion self antigen non-self cell (e.g. bacterium) 'eaten' by **endocytosis** macrophage	• A non-self cell, often a **bacterium**, enters the **blood** and is 'eaten' by a **macrophage**, by **endocytosis**. • Macrophages are a type of white blood cell. • The non-self cell is broken down inside the macrophage.
Antigen presentation non-self antigen	• **Antigens** from the non-self cell are displayed on the surface of the macrophage.
Clonal expansion macrophage T-helper lymphocyte cytokines cell division further cell divisions B-lymphocyte	• Specific **T-helper lymphocytes** and specific **B-lymphocytes** (types of white blood cells) attach to non-self antigens. • A T-helper lymphocyte produces chemicals – **cytokines**. • Cytokines activate the B-lymphocytes that are attached to the macrophage and make them divide, producing a **clone**. • Thus, many B-lymphocytes are produced capable of destroying this particular antigen.
Differentiation B-lymphocyte plasma cell B-memory cell antibody	The cloned B-lymphocytes differentiate into: • either **plasma cells** that produce antibodies specific to the antigen on the cells that entered the body, • or **B-memory cells** that are stored in lymphatic tissue and are able to produce plasma cells very quickly if the same antigen enters the body again.

BLOOD GROUPS

SELF ANTIGENS

- All body cells have **self antigens**.
- There are lots of different self antigens on our cells.
- They are inherited.

Red blood cells have self antigens. To identify blood groups
we refer to two of them:
- antigen A
- antigen B

Red blood cells can have one or the other, both or neither.
Combinations of these self antigens produce 4 possible blood
groups: A, B, AB and O.

Blood group	Antigen A present	Antigen B present
A	✓	✗
B	✗	✓
AB	✓	✓
O	✗	✗

MUST REMEMBER

There are genes for these antigens in all body cells. The genes are only expressed in red blood cells.

ANTIBODIES

The body is capable of producing antibodies against the antigens
it does not possess.
When an antibody meets the corresponding antigen on red blood
cells, it causes the red blood cells to stick together, a response called
agglutination.

- **Antibody a** will cause cells with **antigen A** to stick together.
- **Antibody b** will cause cells with **antigen B** to stick together.

In this system, the body produces antibodies only to those self
antigens that are **not** present on its own red blood cells.

MUST TAKE CARE

Must never use the term 'clot' as an alternative to agglutination.

(Clotting is a totally different biological process and will not get a mark.)

The self antigens and antibodies for each blood group

Blood group	Self antigen	Antibody produced
A	antigen A	antibody b
B	antigen B	antibody a
AB	antigen A and antigen B	none
O	none	antibody a and antibody b

MUST REMEMBER

When deciding whether one blood group can be safely given to someone with a different blood group, always consider the antigens on the red blood cells of the donor.

The antibodies of the donor are not important as they will be diluted and have no effect.

WHO CAN GIVE BLOOD TO WHOM?

- The person who gives the blood is called the **donor**.
- The person who receives the blood is called the **recipient**.
- It is the antigens of the donor that must be taken into account.
- It is the antibodies that the recipient can produce that are important.

Groups that may or may not be used in transfusions

Recipient's blood group	Antibodies in blood	Donor's blood group Antigens on red blood cells			
		A A	B B	AB A and B	O neither A nor B
A	b	✓	✗	✗	✓
B	a	✗	✓	✗	✓
AB	neither a nor b	✓	✓	✓	✓
O	a and b	✗	✗	✗	✓

Key: ✓ transfusion can take place, no agglutination
✗ transfusion cannot take place, agglutination would take place

CROP PLANTS

Crop plants are plants that humans grow for a specific purpose.
They form a major component of the diet of millions of people.
They have been selectively bred to achieve maximum yield.

ADAPTATIONS OF CEREAL PLANTS

Cereals are plants grown for their grain. The most common in Europe are:

- **wheat**, used to make bread and pasta.
- **maize**, eaten as corn on the cob and as sweet corn.

These cereal plants do not grow well in all parts of the world. Other cereal crops, such as **sorghum** and **rice**, are important in different parts of the world.

- In differing environments, different types of plants are grown.
- Different plants are adapted to survive in different conditions.

To yield more grain, a plant must photosynthesise more.

> **MUST REMEMBER**
>
> - In order to photosynthesise, plants need water, carbon dioxide and light (see **A2 Biology Revision Notes**).
> - Cells produce ATP by a process called respiration (see **A2 Biology Revision Notes**). More ATP is produced (in **aerobic respiration**) if oxygen is present than if oxygen is in limited supply or is absent (in **anaerobic respiration**).

A plant requires:	It enters:		But in hot/dry conditions:
carbon dioxide	the leaf through stomata	chloroplast / pore / guard cells — Open / Closed	**water is lost** through the stomata
water	the root through root hairs	root / root hair	water sinks through the soil or evaporates

> **MUST REMEMBER**
>
> In hot/dry conditions there must be a compromise between collecting carbon dioxide and losing water.

RICE

Conditions in which crop plant is adapted to grow	Adaptations
Waterlogged soil This reduces the amount of oxygen available to the roots.	**Stem** has tissue called **aerenchyma** with large air spaces. These spaces: • allow oxygen to diffuse easily to cells in the plant's roots, providing some oxygen for the roots to **respire aerobically**. • provide buoyancy, keeping the photosynthesising leaves in the light. **Root** is shallow. A small volume of oxygen diffuses into it from the soil and the surface water. The root can respire without oxygen, **anaerobically**, and produces **ethanol**. Ethanol is **toxic**, but rice plant cells are **tolerant** of ethanol, so **anaerobic respiration** can continue in rice root cells.

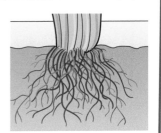

epidermis   air space

aerenchyma

SORGHUM

Conditions in which crop plant is adapted to grow

Adaptations

Hot/dry regions

Their adaptations increase water uptake and/or reduce water loss.

Leaf
- A very thick waxy cuticle reduces water loss by evaporation from leaf surface.
- Having few stomata (or sunken stomata) reduces water loss.
- The leaf rolls inwards, trapping a layer of moist air.

Root
An extensive root system enables water uptake over a large area.

Photosynthesis
Sorghum uses a specialised method of photosynthesis, C_4 pathway. See 'Maize' below.

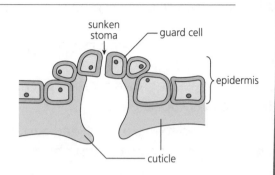

MUST REMEMBER

These leaf modifications *do not stop* water loss; they only **reduce** it.

MAIZE

Conditions in which crop plant is adapted to grow

Adaptations

Hot regions

The stomata are often closed. This helps to reduce water loss but leads to a low carbon dioxide concentration in the leaf.

Leaf
- A very thick waxy cuticle reduces water loss by evaporation from the leaf surface.
- Having few stomata (or sunken stomata) reduces water loss.
- The leaf rolls inwards, trapping a layer of moist air.

Photosynthesis
- Maize plants use a specialised method of photosynthesis, C_4 **pathway**. That is, it makes a 4-carbon compound.
- This enables maize to convert CO_2 to a 4-carbon compound, even in low carbon dioxide concentrations.
- This 4-carbon compound can now be used as a source of carbon dioxide by other photosynthesising cells.

Summary diagram

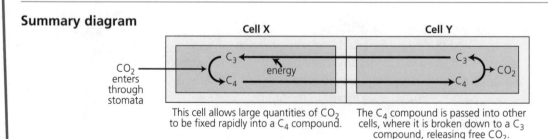

This cell allows large quantities of CO_2 to be fixed rapidly into a C_4 compound.

The C_4 compound is passed into other cells, where it is broken down to a C_3 compound, releasing free CO_2.

MUST REMEMBER

Because the C_4 pathway uses a lot of ATP, it can only occur where light intensities are very high.

CULTIVATING PLANTS

CONTROLLING THE ABIOTIC ENVIRONMENT

Humans are able to control the conditions in which plants grow to get the maximum yield.

> Increasing photosynthesis → Increases the size of the plant → Increases crop yield

FACTORS AFFECTING PHOTOSYNTHESIS

Light intensity	Carbon dioxide concentration
Trend **A** shows that: • increasing light intensity will increase the rate of photosynthesis. • in this region of the graph, light is the limiting factor because if you increase light intensity, photosynthesis increases. Trend **B** shows that: • increasing light intensity does not increase photosynthesis. • Therefore light is not a limiting factor. • Something else becomes the limiting factor, such as carbon dioxide concentration.	Trend **A** shows that: • increasing carbon dioxide concentration will increase the rate of photosynthesis. • in this region of the graph carbon dioxide is the limiting factor because if you increase carbon dioxide, photosynthesis increases. Trend **B** shows that: • increasing carbon dioxide concentration further does not increase photosynthesis. • Therefore carbon dioxide is not a limiting factor. • Something else becomes the limiting factor, such as light intensity.

Summary of the effect of the three factors

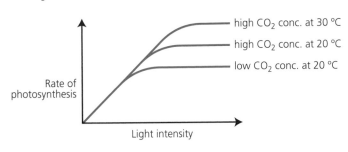

high CO_2 conc. at 30 °C
high CO_2 conc. at 20 °C
low CO_2 conc. at 20 °C

MUST REMEMBER

Temperature speeds up the rate of enzyme-controlled reactions (see page 16), and also speeds up the rate of photosynthesis.

In **greenhouses**, light intensity, carbon dioxide concentration and temperature can be controlled:

Light	Carbon dioxide concentration	Temperature
• an increase in both intensity and duration using lamps • a decrease in intensity using blinds	• an increase using oil burners	• an increase using heaters • a decrease by opening windows

FERTILISERS

Plants photosynthesise to make carbohydrates. To make other compounds such as proteins or DNA, plants also require a supply of mineral ions such as **nitrates** and **phosphates**.

MUST TAKE CARE

Never use the terms nitrogen or phosphorus.

Plants take up these elements only in a soluble, inorganic form such as nitrates and phosphates.

Nitrates are used in the production of proteins, DNA and RNA.

Phosphates are used in the production of DNA, RNA and ATP.

WHY USE FERTILISERS?

In a natural ecosystem	In an agricultural ecosystem
• Mineral ions come from the rocks which gave rise to the soil. • Plants absorb the minerals through their root hairs. • The mineral ions are used in the production of new plant tissues. • Plants die and decay. • Minerals are returned to the soil, ready to be taken up by other plants.	• Crops take up mineral ions from the soil and grow. • However, the crops are then **harvested** (part or all of the plant is removed). • Little or no decomposition takes place. • Little or no mineral ions are returned to the soil.
Result • A balance exists between rate of uptake and rate of return. • There is continued plant growth and no need to add fertilisers.	**Result** • Over time, the soil loses its nutrients and becomes infertile. • There is no plant growth unless the mineral ions are replaced by using fertilisers.

Farmers can use one of two forms to replace these lost mineral ions:

- **Organic** fertiliser includes waste material from farms, e.g. manure, bedding straw and urine.
- **Inorganic** fertilisers (powders produced in factories) contain specific mineral ions.

ORGANIC FERTILISER VERSUS INORGANIC FERTILISER

Organic (natural sources, e.g. manure)		Inorganic (synthesised, containing only minerals)	
Advantage	**Disadvantage**	**Advantage**	**Disadvantage**

• Cheap
• Contains a variety of valuable mineral ions
• Adds organic matter to soil which:
  – improves soil structure
  – reduces erosion
  – improves water-holding properties
• Nutrients are released slowly in decomposition, lessening the problem of leaching.
	• Wet, containing decomposing material with a strong smell
	• Bulky, **so** transported and applied in very large amounts
	• Unknown and variable levels of nutrients
		• Dry, clean with no smell
		• Smaller quantities are needed, **so** they are easily stored, easy to transport and are applied in small amounts.
		• Known nutrient content
		• Even application
			• Expensive to produce and buy
			• Surplus nutrients are washed into streams, pond and lakes – leaching could cause **eutrophication**.
			• Powders do not improve soil quality.
			• Excess could damage plants since direct contact with roots can cause 'burning'.

LEACHING OF NUTRIENTS AND EUTROPHICATION

More inorganic fertiliser is often applied than a crop requires. This leads to:
- **leaching**. The mineral ions dissolve in the soil water and the surplus is washed into waterways.
- **eutrophication**. The build-up of mineral ions in waterways leads to the death of many organisms.

Summary of eutrophication

Fertilisers, especially nitrates and phosphates, are added to land.

↓

Excess fertiliser is leached out by rain into streams and lakes.

↓

Nutrient levels increase in waterways.

↓

The growth of algae increases; they float on the top, producing an **algal bloom**.

↓

The algae block light to plants growing below the surface.

↓

Algae and plants below the surface die, as they cannot photosynthesise.

↓

They are decomposed by aerobic bacteria which then have a population explosion.

↓

Oxygen level in water falls due to respiration of decomposing bacteria.

↓

Organisms that require oxygen (e.g. fish) die.

↓

These decompose and so reduce oxygen levels further.

PESTS

A pest is an organism that reduces the yield of a crop plant.

Pests include **weeds** and **insects**:

A weed is any plant growing where it is not wanted (e.g. a rose in a cornfield).

An insect pest causes direct damage by eating plants.

Weeds	Insect pests
• A weed is an **interspecific competitor**, competing for: – light – nutrients – water – space. • Weed seeds can contaminate a crop after harvesting, – reducing its economic value. – reintroducing weeds into the new crop. • Weeds can be the host for pests and diseases.	• Insect pests destroy the part of the crop that is eaten. • They reduce the amount of leaf tissue, causing: – less photosynthesis – less carbohydrate production – less yield. • They cause disease. Plant viruses are often carried by an insect vector.

PESTICIDES

Several chemicals can be used to remove pests from the crop. These are called **pesticides**. They can be named more specifically after the pest they control.

- **Herbicides** kill weeds.
- **Insecticides** kill insects.
- **Fungicides** kill fungi.

Chemical pesticides

Contact pesticides	Systemic pesticides		Residual pesticides
	Insecticides	Herbicides	
Sprayed onto **crops**	Sprayed onto **crops**	Sprayed onto **crops and weeds**	Sprayed onto **soil**
Must make contact with the pest and are absorbed through the surface of the pest	Absorbed by leaves and are transported around the plant without harming it	Only absorbed and transported through the weeds	
	Kill sap-sucking insects (e.g. aphids) that take up the poison	Kill all tissues, including roots	Kill germinating weed seedlings; also fungal spores, insect eggs and larvae
• Inexpensive • Some pests escape • Short-term effect • Need frequent spraying	• Inexpensive • Specific to pest • Long-term effect • Only applied once		• Inexpensive • Not washed away • Remain active long term • Only applied once

Some long-lasting (**persistent**) pesticides can have a harmful effect on the environment, by accumulating in food chains. This is known as **bioaccumulation**. These pesticides kill non-target organisms, and therefore less toxic and shorter-lived pesticides tend to be used today.

Bioaccumulation

- The pesticide is taken in by the pest.
- It is stored in the pest, not broken down or excreted.
- One predator eats many pests.
- So the pesticide becomes concentrated in the predators.
- These predators are eaten by another predator.

Result
- The poison is passed up the food chain.
- Over time, pesticide levels in the animals increase and may reach lethal concentrations.
- Top predators die.

DDT in:

Tertiary consumer = top predator (carnivore) — **fish-eating birds** (ospreys) 25 ppm

Secondary consumer = predator (carnivore) — **large fish** (needle fish) 2 ppm

Primary consumer (herbivore) — **small fish** (minnows) 0.5 ppm

Producer — **zooplankton** 0.04 ppm

water 0.000 003 ppm

BIOLOGICAL CONTROL OF PESTS

Biological control uses organisms that are the natural predator or parasite of the pest.

- Lacewings are general predators of small insects (aphids) and moths.
- Parasitic wasps lay eggs in larvae of insect pests, the eggs hatch and the offspring eat the pest.

A successful biological control organism is specific and maintains its population in the environment.

Advantages of biological control	Disadvantages of biological control
• It is highly specific, killing only the pest. • It is non-polluting. • It needs be introduced only once. • Once established, it prevents pest infestations for years at no extra cost. • Pests do not become resistant as they would with chemicals.	• It can take months to become effective, and by then the crop may be destroyed. • It is too specific, and if only effective against one pest, crops may be attacked by other pests. • It only keeps pests at a low level - it does not get rid of them completely.

In **integrated pest control**, a variety of methods are used to control pests such as:
- resistant seed varieties
- biological control
- careful use of selected pesticides

CONTROL OF REPRODUCTION

The female reproductive system goes through regular cycles.

- Each cycle is called an **oestrous cycle**.
- The cycle affects two organs: the **ovary** and the **uterus**.
- The ovary is where the follicles develop, each producing an **oocyte** (egg cell) which is released during **ovulation** to be fertilised by sperm.
- The uterus is where the embryo is implanted and the fetus will develop.
- The lining of the uterus is the **endometrium**.

THE OESTROUS CYCLE

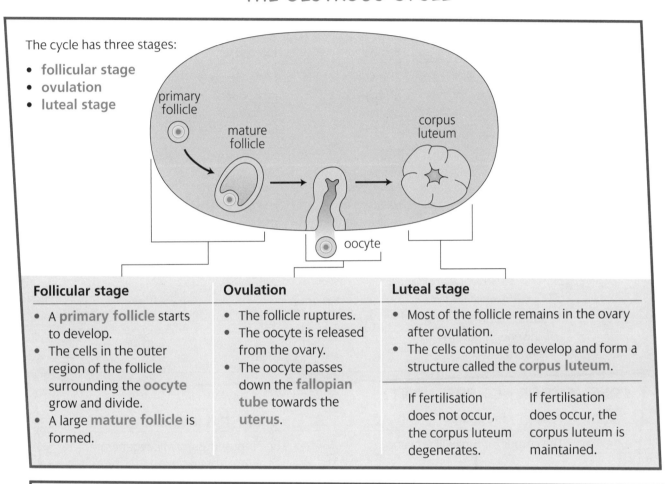

The cycle has three stages:

- **follicular stage**
- **ovulation**
- **luteal stage**

Follicular stage	Ovulation	Luteal stage
• A **primary follicle** starts to develop. • The cells in the outer region of the follicle surrounding the **oocyte** grow and divide. • A large **mature follicle** is formed.	• The follicle ruptures. • The oocyte is released from the ovary. • The oocyte passes down the **fallopian tube** towards the **uterus**.	• Most of the follicle remains in the ovary after ovulation. • The cells continue to develop and form a structure called the **corpus luteum**.

For the luteal stage:

If fertilisation does not occur, the corpus luteum degenerates.	If fertilisation does occur, the corpus luteum is maintained.

HORMONE CONTROL OF THE OESTROUS CYCLE

There are four hormones to remember.

Name of hormone	Where produced	Effect
FSH (Follicle stimulating hormone)	Pituitary gland	Stimulates the: • ovaries to develop follicles
Oestrogen	Ovary • ovarian follicles • corpus luteum	Causes the: • endometrium to grow • pituitary gland to stop producing FSH • pituitary gland to produce LH
LH (Luteinising hormone)	Pituitary gland	Causes the: • mature follicle to rupture and release an oocyte • growth of the corpus luteum to be stimulated
Progesterone	Ovary • corpus luteum	Causes the: • endometrium to be maintained • pituitary gland to stop producing LH

SUMMARY OF HORMONES IN THE OESTROUS CYCLE

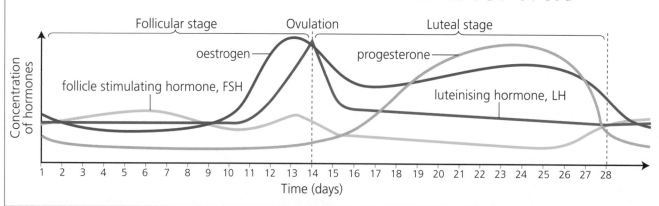

Follicular stage		Ovulation	Luteal stage	
Hormone	**Effect**	**Event**	**Hormone**	**Effect**
FSH is produced by pituitary; concentration increases.	It causes the follicle cells surrounding the oocyte to grow. Follicle cells produce **oestrogen**.	The **surge of LH** brings about ovulation.	Oestrogen is produced by the corpus luteum.	It maintains inhibition of FSH, and FSH concentration stays low.
Oestrogen is produced by follicles; concentration increases.	At **low levels** it inhibits the release of FSH, and FSH concentration falls. At **high levels** it stimulates the production of LH, and LH concentration increases. It stimulates the growth of the endometrium of the uterus.	An oocyte is released from a mature follicle.	**Progesterone** is produced by the corpus luteum. Its concentration increases	With oestrogen it inhibits FSH and LH. It maintains the growth of the endometrium of the uterus.

PREGNANT OR NOT PREGNANT?

Pregnant	Not pregnant
The corpus luteum will remain. ↓	The corpus luteum will degenerate. (breakdown) ↓
Oestrogen and progesterone will continue to be produced. ↓	Oestrogen and progesterone will not be produced, so levels decrease. ↓
They will continue to inhibit the release from the pituitary of FSH and LH. ↓	Inhibition on the pituitary is removed so FSH can be released. ↓
The endometrium will not break down and will provide nutrients for the implanted embryo.	The endometrium will break down and be removed in the menstrual flow.

MUST REMEMBER

This information is based on the human cycle.

It is important to understand the principles and be able to apply them to any mammal.
- FSH always stimulates follicles to be produced.
- LH stimulates ovulation and the development of the corpus luteum.
- Oestrogen inhibits FSH.
- Progesterone with oestrogen inhibits FSH and LH.

OESTRUS IN FARM ANIMALS

- As well as physiological changes, the behaviour of female mammals changes around the time of ovulation. The period of these changes is called the **oestrus**.
- These changes are brought about mainly by oestrogen.
- Commonly the female mammal is said to be 'on heat'.
- These changes can be recognised and used by a farmer to indicate the correct time for the animal to be inseminated.

SOME CHANGES SEEN IN A COW

Physiological changes	Behavioural changes
• Dilation of neck of uterus • Change in texture of mucus – becomes thinner and more slimy	• Increased restlessness: the cow moves about more and feeds less • Mounting other cattle • Decreased aggression towards other members of the herd

MUST REMEMBER

Only changes at oestrus in **one mammal** need be remembered.

The cow is an easy example.

CONTROLLING HUMAN FERTILITY

Hormones are used to control human fertility:

- as **contraceptives**
- to treat **infertility**

CONTRACEPTIVES

Type of contraceptive pill	Effect
Combined pill: • contains both oestrogen and progesterone • is taken daily	• Increases levels of these hormones in the blood. • They inhibit the release of FSH from the pituitary. • There is no FSH to stimulate the follicles to develop. • No ovulation occurs.
Mini pill: • contains small amounts of progesterone • is taken daily	• It stops production of the oocyte, • by interfering with meiosis.
Morning after pill: • contains high concentrations of progesterone • is taken up to 72 hours after intercourse	• It stops implantation.

MUST TAKE CARE

Progesterone alone does not inhibit ovulation.

INFERTILITY

There are many causes of infertility.
Both men and women can be infertile.
Failing to ovulate is one of the most common forms of infertility in females.
If so, they can be treated in one of two ways:

FSH

Giving the woman FSH will stimulate her ovaries.
↓
Follicles will develop.
↓
She will ovulate and release an oocyte.

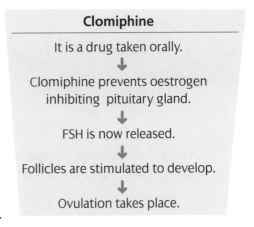

Clomiphine

It is a drug taken orally.
↓
Clomiphine prevents oestrogen inhibiting pituitary gland.
↓
FSH is now released.
↓
Follicles are stimulated to develop.
↓
Ovulation takes place.

The technique above is often used in IVF treatment:
- The oocytes are collected and fertilised by sperm in the laboratory.
- The fertilised oocyte is then replaced into the uterus.

CONTROLLING REPRODUCTION OF DOMESTIC ANIMALS

Domestic animals are kept for their:
- meat production e.g. cows, sheep and pigs.
- eggs e.g. chickens and ducks.
- milk e.g. cows, sheep and goats.

It is important that domestic animals produce as much as possible so that there will be more and cheaper food for humans.

Their productivity can be increased by using hormones.
There are three main ways that this can be achieved:

Transplanting embryos	Synchronised breeding	Increasing milk yield in cows
This allows a large number of females (often cows) to become pregnant with embryos from another female that carries a desirable characteristic.	It is often cost effective to: • inseminate at the same time. • give birth at the same time.	More milk produced by each cow means a greater total yield.
Example The donor cow is injected with **FSH** and **LH**. ↓ The cow produces many follicles. ↓ The cow is artificially inseminated. ↓ Embryos are removed from the cow after 6 days. ↓ The embryos are then put into the uterus of another cow.	**Example** A flock of sheep treated with **progesterone**, using a coil placed into the vagina. ↓ The corpus luteum is maintained and continues to produce oestrogen and progesterone. ↓ These inhibit **FSH** – sheep cannot become pregnant. ↓ Treatment is stopped, by removing the coil. ↓ The corpus luteum degenerates – no oestrogen or progesterone is made. ↓ Inhibition of FSH is removed. ↓ Sheep now produce FSH. ↓ All sheep will now ovulate at the same time.	**Example** The cow is injected with **BST** – **bovine somatotrophin**. ↓ This stimulates the growth of the cow's udder. ↓ More milk can be produced and stored in the udder.

For practice in answering AS Biology questions, why not use *Collins Exam Practice AS Biology*?

GENE TECHNOLOGY

POLYMERASE CHAIN REACTION, PCR

It can be difficult to obtain large quantities of DNA. This technique:

- is used to increase the amount of DNA present.
- involves repeated **DNA replication**.

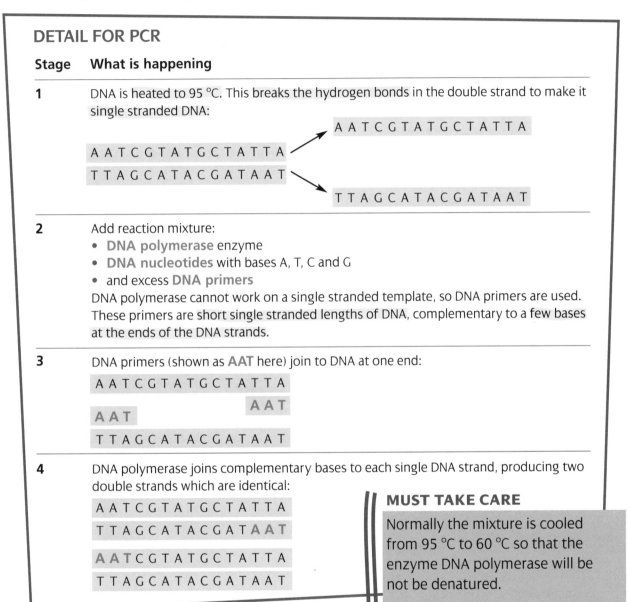

DETAIL FOR PCR

Stage	What is happening
1	DNA is heated to 95 °C. This breaks the hydrogen bonds in the double strand to make it single stranded DNA:
2	Add reaction mixture: • **DNA polymerase** enzyme • **DNA nucleotides** with bases A, T, C and G • and excess **DNA primers** DNA polymerase cannot work on a single stranded template, so DNA primers are used. These primers are short single stranded lengths of DNA, complementary to a few bases at the ends of the DNA strands.
3	DNA primers (shown as **AAT** here) join to DNA at one end:
4	DNA polymerase joins complementary bases to each single DNA strand, producing two double strands which are identical:

MUST TAKE CARE

Normally the mixture is cooled from 95 °C to 60 °C so that the enzyme DNA polymerase will be not be denatured.

However, thermostable enzymes are now commonly used. These can still operate at high temperatures.

SUMMARY OF PCR

Separate the strands of DNA (heat to 95 °C).

↓

Add reaction mixture:
primers, DNA nucleotides and DNA polymerase.

↓

Incubate (cool to 60 °C): DNA replicates.

The number of extra strands of DNA increases slowly at first, but after a few cycles, millions of DNA molecules can be produced from a single strand.

It is possible to use this material for genetic fingerprinting.

PCR cycles	No. of DNA strands
1	2
2	4
3	8
4	16
5	32
10	1 024
15	32 768
20	1 048 576
25	33 554 432

CYSTIC FIBROSIS AND GENE THERAPY

Cystic fibrosis is caused by a defective gene which affects mucus-producing glands. The mucus produced is much thicker than normal.

In the **lungs**
- Mucus blocks airways and increases the chance of lung infections.

In the **pancreas**
- Mucus blocks ducts along which digestive enzymes pass to the gut.
- The pancreas reacts by forming fluid filled sacs, called cysts, hence cystic.
- Eventually the pancreas degenerates and becomes fibrous, hence fibrosis.

Normal gene	Defective gene
This gene codes for the cystic fibrosis transmembrane regulator or (**CFTR**) **protein**.	This gene causes the CFTR protein to have one amino acid (phenylalanine) missing.
CFTR is found in surface membranes of cells in the lungs and gut.	
CFTR is an ion channel which allows transport of **chloride ions** out of cells.	The ion channel does not work – chloride ions cannot pass out of cells.
This causes osmosis. Water leaves the cells and thins the mucus.	No osmosis takes place. Thick mucus is formed.

GENE THERAPY

The normal form of the gene can be introduced into lung cells:
- in a harmless virus – the virus introduces any genetic material into these cells.
- wrapped in lipid molecules – these cells take lipids through their membranes.

The cells with the normal gene will now function properly.

MUST REMEMBER
- A virus is specific to one type of cell (or a few types).
- During its normal life cycle, a virus will introduce its genetic material into the host cell.
- The virus delivers any genetic material it contains, including the normal gene for CTFR.

DIGESTION

A definition of **digestion**:

> Foods containing large organic insoluble molecules,
> such as proteins, carbohydrates and lipids, are broken
> down by hydrolysis into small organic soluble molecules
> such as amino acids, sugars, fatty acids and glycerol.

Reason for digestion: So that food materials can be **absorbed** and transported to every cell of the body.

STRUCTURE AND FUNCTION OF THE GUT WALL

The gut wall has three main layers:

- outer layer – **muscle**
- middle layer – **submucosa**
- inner layer – **mucosa**

Region of gut	Appearance	Special features and function		
		Muscle	**Submucosa**	**Mucosa**
Oesophagus	longitudinal — muscle / submucosa / mucosa / circular	Two layers – for **peristalsis**	It contains glands secreting mucus – which lubricates food for its easy passage.	It has many layers of flattened cells – which protect the submucosa.
Stomach	muscle / submucosa / mucosa / oblique / gastric pit	Three layers – to mix food with enzymes	It separates the other layers.	There is a thick layer with **gastric pits** – which secrete: • mucus • hydrochloric acid • enzyme. (continued)

MUST TAKE CARE

The stomach enzyme pepsin is released as pepsinogen. This is the inactive form and so does not digest the cells of the stomach wall.

Region of gut	Appearance	Special features and function		
		Muscle	**Submucosa**	**Mucosa**
Duodenum		Two layers – for **peristalsis**	It contains **Brunner's glands** – • which secrete alkaline fluid to neutralise stomach acid • and are folded to form **villi**, increasing surface area for absorption.	It contains **goblet cells** – which secrete mucus. Enzymes occur in the **membrane** of the epithelial cells.
Ileum		Two layers – for **peristalsis**	Villi are present. It has many lymph and blood vessels – which absorb digested molecules.	It contains **goblet cells**. It contains **Paneth cells** – which help protect the body from bacterial infection.

DIGESTIVE ENZYMES

Site of production	Enzyme produced	Substrate digested	Product produced
Salivary gland	amylase	starch	maltose
Stomach (gastric pit)	endopeptidase (pepsin)	protein	polypeptides
Pancreas	amylase	starch	maltose
	lipase	lipids	fatty acids and glycerol
	endopeptidase (trypsin)	protein	polypeptides
Small intestine (duodenum/ileum)	exopeptidases	polypeptides	dipeptides and amino acids
	maltase	maltose	glucose

MUST REMEMBER

Bile is NOT an enzyme.

• It is produced by the liver and stored in the gall bladder.
• It contains:
  – an alkali, sodium hydrogencarbonate, which neutralises stomach acid
  – bile salts which emulsify lipids.

MUST TAKE CARE

Endopeptidase hydrolyses peptide bonds in the MIDDLE of a polypeptide chain.
Exopeptidase hydrolyses peptide bonds at the END of a polypeptide chain.

ABSORPTION

When digestion is complete, the products, sugars, amino acids, fatty acids and glycerol are absorbed from the small intestine into the blood or lymph system.

Digested product absorbed	How does it happen?
Amino acids and glucose move into a **blood vessel**.	**Amino acids and glucose:** • move from the small intestine by **facilitated diffusion**. • are linked to **sodium ions**. • move into the blood by **facilitated diffusion**. Sodium ions: • are removed by **active transport**.
Salts and water move into a **blood vessel**.	**Salts:** • move from the gut by **facilitated diffusion**. • move into the blood by **active transport**. **Water** moves down a water potential gradient created by salts: • moving from the gut by diffusion (**osmosis**). • moving into the blood by diffusion (**osmosis**).
Fatty acids and glycerol move into **lymph vessel**.	**Fatty acids and glycerol:** • move from the gut by **diffusion**. They recombine in the epithelium cell to form a **triglyceride** (lipid). **Triglycerides:** • move into the lymph by **diffusion**.

MUST REMEMBER

As lipid is not soluble in water, it is coated by protein in the lacteal forming a **chylomicron** (lipoprotein), and circulates in this form in the blood.

EXTRACELLULAR DIGESTION

- The food of **fungi** is also made up of large, organic and insoluble molecules.
- Many fungi are called **saprophytes** because they feed on dead plants and animals.
- Fungi digest their food outside their cells and absorb the soluble products.
  This is called **extracellular digestion**.

EXTRACELLULAR DIGESTION

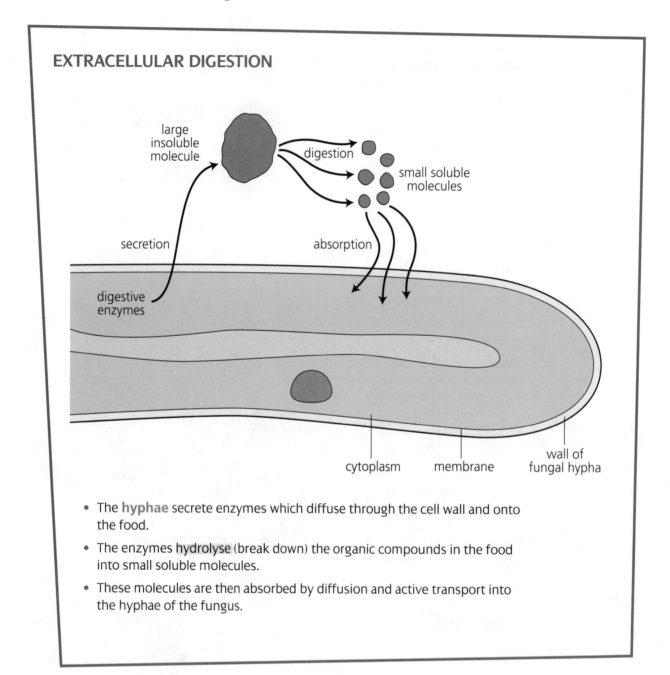

- The **hyphae** secrete enzymes which diffuse through the cell wall and onto the food.
- The enzymes hydrolyse (break down) the organic compounds in the food into small soluble molecules.
- These molecules are then absorbed by diffusion and active transport into the hyphae of the fungus.

MUST TAKE CARE

Much of the digestion in a mammal occurs outside cells of the body, but within the cavity of the gut.

This is also **extracellular digestion**.

GAS EXCHANGE IN FISH AND PLANTS

See 'The lungs and ventilation', pages 27–29, for gas exchange in mammals.

GENERAL POINTS

- **Gas exchange** takes place by diffusion.
- Oxygen is taken in and carbon dioxide is removed.
- To increase the rate of diffusion, the **exchange surface** must:
  1. have a large surface area.
  2. be thin.
  3. maintain a concentration gradient.

FISH

- Fish extract oxygen from the water using **gills**.
- Oxygen circulates in the blood to all cells.

---

1. **Surface area**
   Gills:
   - have many **lamellae**.
   - are covered by **gill plates**.

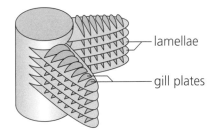

lamellae

gill plates

---

2. **Thickness**
   Only two cells are between the blood and water: the distance that oxygen must travel is very short.

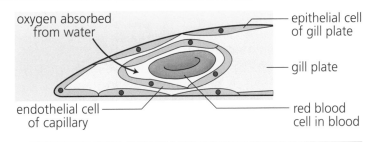

oxygen absorbed from water

epithelial cell of gill plate

gill plate

endothelial cell of capillary

red blood cell in blood

---

3. **Concentration gradient**
   - Water containing oxygen moves across the gill.
   - Blood containing oxygen moves out of gill.
   - In the gill, blood and oxygen pass one another in opposite directions.
     = **counter-current mechanism**

   This makes sure that a diffusion gradient between blood and water is always maintained.

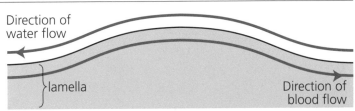

Direction of water flow

lamella

Direction of blood flow

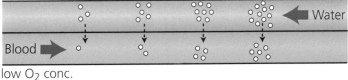

high O$_2$ conc.

Water

Blood

low O$_2$ conc.

MUST REMEMBER

As both gases (oxygen and carbon dioxide) move by diffusion, the mechanism to remove carbon dioxide from the blood is the same as that to obtain oxygen from the environment.

PLANTS

- Plants are less active than animals and require less oxygen for respiration.
- Root and stem cells obtain oxygen dissolved in the water taken up by roots.
- Leaves extract oxygen from air, so must avoid excess water loss at the same time.
- Most of the plant surface is covered by a waterproof waxy cuticle.

1. **Surface area**
   Leaves have:

   - **spongy mesophyll**
     - has irregularly shaped cells with many air spaces between them.
     - has many cells in contact with the air in the leaf.

   - **stomata**
     - are holes in the epidermis between two **guard cells**.
     - The guard cells can change shape to open or close the stomata.

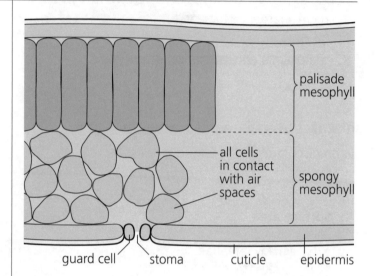

2. **Thickness**
   There is only a thin permeable cellulose wall and cell membrane between air and the cytoplasm of cells.

3. **Concentration gradient**
   Oxygen is used by cells of the leaf during respiration, or is moved from cell to cell by diffusion.

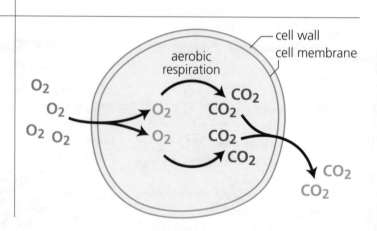

MUST REMEMBER

- When LIGHT is present, photosynthesis occurs.
- It is a more active process than respiration.
- During photosynthesis, carbon dioxide is used and oxygen is produced.
- Due to the concentration gradient, CO_2 moves into the leaf cells and O_2 moves out.

OXYGEN DISSOCIATION CURVES

One function of the blood is to transport substances, including:

- oxygen to the cells.
- carbon dioxide away from the cells.

TRANSPORTING OXYGEN

Haemoglobin:

- is the pigment found in red blood cells.
- is a protein combined with haem, a non-protein part.
- It combines reversibly with oxygen.

In high oxygen concentrations, such as capillaries in the lungs, haemoglobin and oxygen combine to form oxyhaemoglobin.

In low oxygen concentrations, such as capillaries in active organs and tissues, oxyhaemoglobin dissociates: it releases oxygen.

OXYGEN DISSOCIATION CURVE

The oxygen dissociation curve demonstrates why haemoglobin is such an efficient molecule for transporting oxygen.

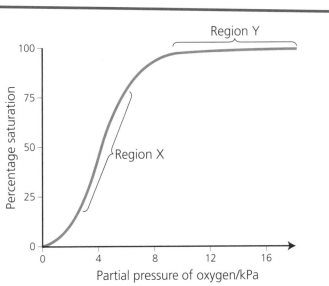

DESCRIPTION OF THE GRAPH

As the partial pressure of oxygen increases, the oxygen that combines with haemoglobin increases, but by different amounts at different partial pressures.

Region X

- These are the oxygen concentrations found in active cells.
- There is less oxygen combined with haemoglobin.
- The graph shows that oxyhaemoglobin releases oxygen at these levels.

Region Y

- These high oxygen concentrations are found in the lungs.

- The graph shows that haemoglobin combines readily with oxygen, forming oxyhaemoglobin.

MUST REMEMBER

As the partial pressure of oxygen decreases by only a small amount, there is a **steep fall** in the graph.

This means that a slight fall in oxygen concentration produces a large increase in oxyhaemoglobin dissociation (lots of oxygen is released).

MUST TAKE CARE

Partial pressure of oxygen represents the amount of oxygen present. Therefore, the more oxygen the higher the partial pressure.

Percentage saturation represents how much oxygen is being carried by the haemoglobin.

EFFECT OF CARBON DIOXIDE CONCENTRATION

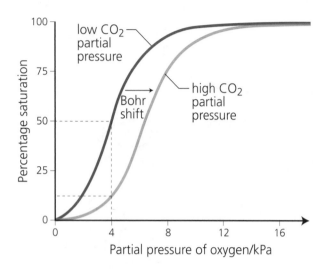

Example

At a partial pressure of oxygen of 4 kPa:

- **low CO$_2$ partial pressure**
  – haemoglobin is 50% saturated
  ∴ has given up 50% of its oxygen

- **high CO$_2$ partial pressure**
  – haemoglobin is 12.5% saturated
  ∴ has given up 87.5% of its oxygen,
  so RELEASING MORE OXYGEN

- With increased amounts of carbon dioxide, the curve shifts to the right.
- This is called the **Bohr shift**.

The effect is that at the same partial pressure of oxygen, more oxygen will be released. Why does this happen?

- Carbon dioxide is a waste product of respiration.
- The more respiration occurring, the more carbon dioxide produced.
- The carbon dioxide combines with haemoglobin,
- changing the shape of haemoglobin,
- which releases more of its oxygen.

EFFECT OF CHANGING pH

- Carbon dioxide released as a waste product of respiration combines with water to form an acid, **carbonic acid**, so:
- the more acidic (lower pH) the blood becomes, the more the curve will shift to the right, and therefore
- more oxygen is released.

MUST REMEMBER

Blood pH is usually maintained around pH 7 by **buffers**.

Haemoglobin is one of the buffers in the blood.

SEXUAL REPRODUCTION

Sexual reproduction involves the joining of two cells, one from the male and one from the female.

If these cells were normal body cells, the number of chromosomes in body cells would double each generation.

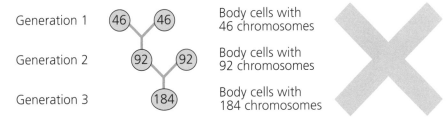

This does not happen.

The nucleus of body cells undergoes a special type of division called meiosis to form cells with half the number of chromosomes – **gametes** (sperm and ova).

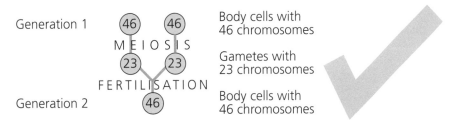

This allows a constant chromosome number to be maintained from one generation to the next.

MEIOSIS

Simple summary of the stages	Illustration
One body cell in a sex organ contains pairs of homologous chromosomes. (Only two pairs are shown for simplicity.)	homologous pair of chromosomes
One sex cell or gamete contains one of each pair of the homologous chromosomes.	one member of a pair of homologous chromosomes

MUST REMEMBER

All species have a different but constant number of chromosomes in their **body cells**.

- Body cells contain pairs of chromosomes called **homologous pairs**.
- The total number of chromosomes is called the **diploid** number (2*n*).
- In humans, 2*n* is 46.

MUST REMEMBER

All species have a different but constant number of chromosomes in their **sex cells**.

- Gametes contain **one member of each pair** of homologous chromosomes.
- The number of chromosomes is called the **haploid** number (*n*).
- In humans, *n* is 23.

DIFFERENCES BETWEEN GAMETES IN HUMANS

Characteristic	Male gamete – sperm	Female gamete – ovum
Structure	 A specialised cell made up of: • head • middle piece • tail	 A simple cell with no special features
Relative sizes	• The head of the sperm is 5 µm long and 2.5 µm across. • It is the smallest cell.	• The ovum is 100 µm in diameter. • It is the largest cell.
Fertilisation		
Number produced	• Approximately 300 000 000 are produced every day. • Each ejaculation may contain twice that number.	• Approximately 400 will be released into the oviduct – one a month.
Mobility	• The **middle piece** contains mitochondria which produces ATP providing energy for movement. • The **tail** spins like a propeller, moving the sperm. • The sperm is **motile**.	• The ovum moves down the oviduct as the result of **cilia** on the **epithelial cells** lining this tube. • The ovum has no structures to let it move unaided. • The ovum is **sessile**.

MUST REMEMBER

Chromatin – DNA present in the nucleus of a cell not undergoing mitosis or meiosis.

Chromatid – one of the two strands of genetic material that make up a chromosome at the beginning of mitosis or meiosis.

Chromosome – a tightly coiled length of DNA, only present during mitosis/meiosis

Centromere – the region on a chromosome which holds the sister chromatids together during the early stages of cell division. It also attaches the chromosome to the spindle fibres.

Centriole – structure found in animal cells which forms the spindle fibres

MUTATION

- Errors can occur during DNA replication.
- A change in the order of bases is called a **gene mutation**.

Definitions to understand

gene	length of DNA found at a particular place (locus) on a chromosome
allele	a different form of a gene
mutation	a change in the DNA of a cell

Therefore mutations could produce different alleles which will result in a different characteristic and this is important in the process of **evolution**.

TYPES OF MUTATION

Chromosomal mutation

- Sections of chromosomes can be lost, or moved to other chromosomes.
- Whole chromosomes or whole sets of chromosomes could be duplicated.

Many crop plants such as tobacco and sugar beet contain extra whole sets of chromosomes = **polyploidy**. Down's syndrome is the result of one extra chromosome number 21 = **trisomy**.

Gene mutation

Change in the sequence of bases of the DNA in one gene, sometimes called a **point mutation**.

Addition: An extra nucleotide is added, so an extra base is added to the sequence.

Deletion: A nucleotide is lost.

Substitution: A nucleotide is replaced by a nucleotide with a different base.

EFFECT OF GENE MUTATION ON GENE EXPRESSION

- Each triplet of bases codes for a specific amino acid.
- The order of the triplets determines the order of the amino acids, and therefore the structure of the protein synthesised by the cell.

MUST REMEMBER

Additions and deletions may cause such **major changes to a protein** that the mutation proves fatal.

Sickle-cell anaemia is caused by the substitution of a single nucleotide in the gene that codes for the protein haemoglobin. Mutations are caused by: X-rays; gamma rays; UV light; cigarette smoke; mustard gas.

NORMAL GENE EXPRESSION

Normal base sequence:

A T C | G A G | T A C | A A G

Codes for: amino acid 1–amino acid 2–amino acid 3–amino acid 4

(aa 1)　　(aa 2)　　(aa 3)　　(aa 4)

EFFECTS OF MUTATIONS

Addition mutation	Deletion mutation	Substitution mutation
Here the second triplet gains the base adenine:	Here the second triplet loses the base guanine:	Here in the second triplet the base thymine replaces the base guanine:
A T C | A G A | G T A | C A A | G	A T C | A G T | A C A | A G	A T C | T A G | T A C | A A G
Codes for:	Codes for:	Codes for:
aa 1—aa 5—aa 6—aa 7	aa 1—aa 8—aa 9	aa 1—aa 10—aa 3—aa 4
• Each triplet following the addition is different. • These triplets code for different amino acids. • This causes a **frame shift**.	• Each triplet following the deletion is different. • These triplets code for different amino acids. • This causes a **frame shift**.	• Only one triplet is different. • It alone codes for a different amino acid. • Each triplet following the substitution remains unchanged. • These triplets code for the same amino acids.
Result: Protein structure is different.	**Result:** Protein structure is different.	**Result:** Protein structure is slightly different.

APPLICATIONS OF CLONING

Definition: A clone is a genetically identical organism.

- Identical twins are clones.
- Clones can be formed naturally when plants reproduce **asexually**.
- Since clones share the characteristics of their parents, a clone will have the positive features of its parents, e.g. fruit flavour, flower scent and colour, growth rate, resistance to disease.

CLONING METHODS

VEGETATIVE PROPAGATION

Type	Detail
• Tubers	Each potato tuber is a swollen stem which grows into a new plant.
• Runners	Strawberries send out stems which lie on the ground: runners. At intervals the stem develops roots and leaves which become a new plant.
• Cuttings	Pieces of stem placed in the soil will often form a root system and develop into a new plant. Rooting chemicals may be used to encourage root growth.
• Grafts	A piece of one plant can be attached to the rootstock of another plant. Many apple varieties are grown like this.

Advantages
- Vegetative propagation maintains genetic stability.
- Mature plants usually develop more quickly.
- Plants grow at the same rate, so can be harvested at the same time.
- It is often easier and therefore cheaper than collecting and sowing seeds.

Disadvantages
- Clones are more difficult to transport than seeds.
- They are more prone to damage or rotting during storage.
- They are more likely to carry disease and, being all the same, they will all be equally affected.

MICROPROPAGATION

Type	Detail
• Tissue culturing	• Small pieces of leaf are taken. • They are placed on a growth medium containing chemicals to encourage shoot growth. • They are then placed on another medium that encourages root growth. • When big enough, they are placed in pots. Oil palm trees are grown like this.

Advantages
- Many plantlets come from one parent.
- The process is rapid.
- Little space is required.
- Environmental conditions can be controlled for maximum growth.
- Sterile hybrids can be propagated.
- Plantlets are disease free.

Disadvantages
- All plants could get the same diseases.
- Growth in a lab is expensive, so it is only worthwhile with expensive plants.

ANIMAL CLONING

Mammals do not reproduce asexually, so, to produce many identical animals, cloning must be done artificially.

Type	Detail
• Embryo transplants	• Eggs are removed from a female with favourable characteristics. • They are fertilised with sperm from a male with favourable characteristics. • They are cultured into an embryo of 16 cells. • The nucleus is removed from each cell. • Each nucleus is used to replace the nucleus from egg cells of other females – the **surrogate mothers**. • These cells are grown into embryos. • Embryos are placed in the uterus of the surrogate mothers.

TRANSPORT IN PLANTS

All plants are multicellular and therefore materials have to be transported into and away from every cell.

MAIN POINTS ON TRANSPORT BY PLANTS

What	How	Section of root
Water	• Water is absorbed by the **roots** where the cuticle is thin. – Most of the plant is covered by a waterproof **waxy cuticle**. – The waxy cuticle cuts down water loss, but also stops water uptake. • Water is transported by a special tissue called **xylem**. • It is lost through holes in the leaves – **stomata**.	
Mineral salts	• Mineral salts are absorbed in solution with water. • Minerals are transported in the water in xylem. **Summary**: Water and mineral salts are transported in one direction: from root to stem and leaves.	
Organic molecules	• **Photosynthesis** results in the production of carbohydrates. • Photosynthesis takes place mainly in **leaves**. • Carbohydrates (e.g. sucrose) are transported by a special tissue called **phloem**: – from leaves to storage areas (roots) or growing areas (new leaves or flowers), or – from storage areas to growing areas. **Summary**: Carbohydrates are transported in both directions; from root to stem and leaves, and from leaves to root.	

root hairs

ROOT STRUCTURE

Area of root	Function
Epidermis	**Root cross section** epidermis: with root hairs cortex: storage parenchyma endodermis: with Casparian bands vascular cylinder: with xylem and phloem tissue epidermis root hair **Extensions of epidermal cells** form **root hairs**. Root hairs: • make contact with more water. • increase the surface area for absorption. **MUST REMEMBER** • Active uptake of minerals into cytoplasm occurs by root hair cells. • There are more minerals inside the cytoplasm than in the soil. Therefore movement is **AGAINST a concentration gradient**.

Cortex	**Irregularly shaped cells**
	• There are many spaces between cells.
	• The spaces are filled with water.
	
	Water can travel from epidermis to endodermis through cell walls and the water-filled spaces:
	  – by the **apoplastic pathway**.
	  – down a water potential gradient.
	
	Water can also travel from cell to cell through the cytoplasm:
	  – by the **symplastic pathway**.
	  – through plasmodesmata.
	
	apoplastic pathway root hair
	symplastic pathway
	plasmodesma
	xylem vessel
	Casparian band
	epidermis cortex endodermis

Endodermis	**Single layer of cells** Cell walls at right angles with the surface are thickened with a waterproof waxy strip, the **Casparian band**. Casparian band cell walls at right angles to root surface The Casparian band prevents water from going through the endodermis by the apoplastic pathway. **Result:** Water travels through the endodermis by the symplastic pathway.

(continued)

Area of root	Function
Xylem	• Xylem consists of elongated, hollow cells (like straws). • Cells have a secondary wall of lignin which stops the cell from collapsing when contents are under pressure. • Xylem carries water through the root into the stem.

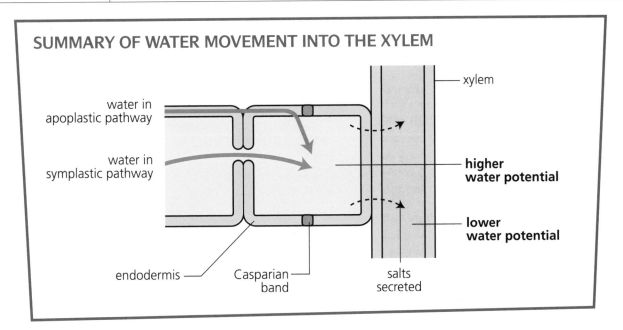

SUMMARY OF WATER MOVEMENT INTO THE XYLEM

water in apoplastic pathway

water in symplastic pathway

endodermis — Casparian band

xylem

higher water potential

lower water potential

salts secreted

WATER MOVEMENT THROUGH THE XYLEM UP THE STEM

Mechanisms causing water movement	Explanation
Root pressure	Movement of water across the roots and into the xylem creates this pressure. • The pressure will only move water a short distance. **Evidence: Water exudes from the top of a small plant when cut.**
Cohesion-tension	Water molecules are polar - they stick to one another by: • cohesion If one molecule moves, it pulls other molecules, creating: • tension Water also sticks to the walls of the xylem, by: • adhesion which holds the column of water together. **Evidence: The diameter of a tree decreases during the day as water rises.**
Transpiration	Transpiration is the loss of water vapour, mainly through the stomata of leaves. As water leaves the leaf it creates a suction pressure, removing water from the top of the xylem. **Evidence: Environmental factors that affect transpiration also affect water movement.**

TRANSPIRATION

- Water moves down a **water potential gradient**.
- The air inside the leaf is always saturated and therefore has a high water potential.
- Any environmental factor which produces a lower water potential will cause transpiration.

Factors affecting transpiration	How transpiration is increased
Air movements	**Increased air movement** • This brings dry air in contact with the leaf. • The air has a lower water potential than the air inside the leaf, • creating a greater water potential gradient, • so more water can be removed.
Humidity	**Low humidity** • This causes the air to hold little water. • The air has a lower water potential than the air inside the leaf, • creating a greater water potential gradient, • so more water can be removed.
Temperature	**High temperature** • This gives more kinetic energy to water molecules. • They are more likely to move away from the plant, • creating a greater water potential gradient, • so more water can be removed.
Light	**High light intensity** • This causes stomata to open. • More saturated air can escape the leaf, • so more water can be removed.

XEROPHYTES

Xerophytes are plants adapted to survive in dry conditions.
All adaptations reduce water loss.

Xerophytic adaptation	Effect
Thick waxy cuticle	Better waterproofing
Needle-shaped leaves	Smaller surface area, reduces water loss
Stomata: • reduced number • in pits • in grooves • only on bottom surface of leaf • shut during the day	Reduce transpiration
Leaves rolled	Smaller surface area, reduces water loss Stomata inside curl, reduces water loss
Leaves reduced to spines	Smaller surface area, reduces water loss Trap layer of moist air, reduces water loss
Succulent stems	Store water
Roots can be deep and shallow	Collect any available water

MUST REMEMBER

Dry condition are not only found in deserts:

- In cold areas, water will be frozen.
- Sandy areas have little water since it drains away.
- Soil in sand dunes also has a high water potential due to the high salt levels, removing water from plants.

MUST TAKE CARE

A waxy cuticle only **reduces** water loss – it **does not stop it**.

MOVEMENT OF ORGANIC SUBSTANCES THROUGH PLANTS

- As an example of organic substances moving through plants, carbohydrates (sucrose) move in phloem tissue.

STRUCTURE OF PHLOEM

Feature	Effect
Elongated cells – joined end to end to form a tube	Fewer walls to obstruct solute passage
Thin cellulose cell walls	Permeable to water and solutes
Sieve plates in end walls	Free movement of solutes between cells
Living cells – no nucleus, but cells do contain other organelles	Free movement of solutes in the cytoplasm
Associated with companion cells via plasmodesmata	Companion cells provide the energy for some of the transport of the solutes and their loading.

sieve plate

plasmodesma

companion cell

sieve tube element

MUST REMEMBER

- A solute is any substance that can dissolve in water.
- Solutes are usually small soluble substances such as sucrose and amino acids.
- An increase in the concentration of solutes will decrease the water potential.

For practice in answering AS Biology questions, why not use *Collins Exam Practice AS Biology*?

SUGGESTED TRANSPORT MECHANISM

In the **mass flow hypothesis**, molecules move from a **source** (where they are loaded into the phloem) to a **sink** (where they are unloaded from the phloem).

- The source is an area of high concentration and could be a leaf or a root.
- The sink is an area of low concentration and could be a root or a growth area.

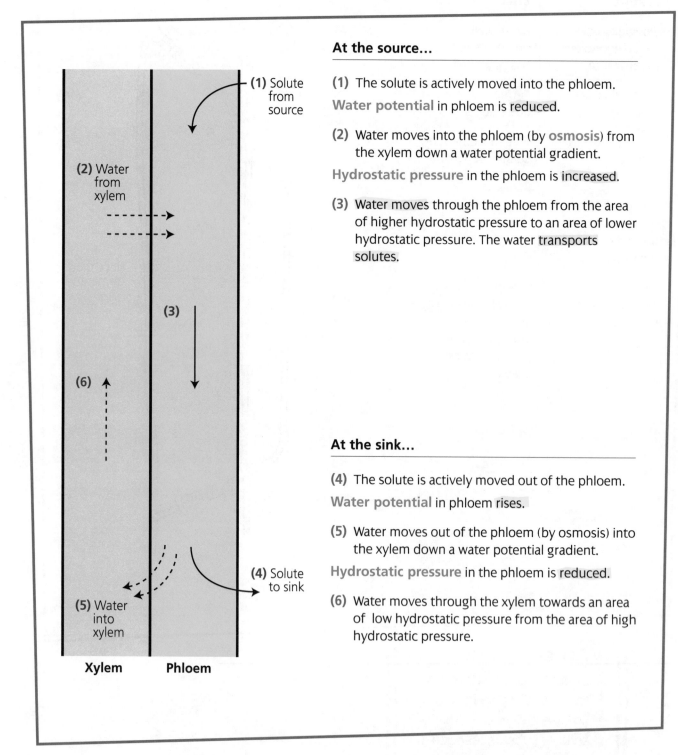

At the source...

(1) The solute is actively moved into the phloem.

Water potential in phloem is **reduced**.

(2) Water moves into the phloem (by **osmosis**) from the xylem down a water potential gradient.

Hydrostatic pressure in the phloem is **increased**.

(3) Water moves through the phloem from the area of higher hydrostatic pressure to an area of lower hydrostatic pressure. The water **transports solutes**.

At the sink...

(4) The solute is actively moved out of the phloem.

Water potential in phloem **rises**.

(5) Water moves out of the phloem (by osmosis) into the xylem down a water potential gradient.

Hydrostatic pressure in the phloem is **reduced**.

(6) Water moves through the xylem towards an area of low hydrostatic pressure from the area of high hydrostatic pressure.

Diagram labels:

(1) Solute from source

(2) Water from xylem

(3)

(6)

(4) Solute to sink

(5) Water into xylem

Xylem　　**Phloem**

EXPERIMENTAL EVIDENCE

Experiment	What did it prove?
Respiratory inhibitors **In a root** • Respiratory inhibitors were applied. • The rate of ions uptake was measured. • There was little ion uptake compared to a plant with no respiratory inhibitor.	Ion uptake into the root is by active transport.
Ringing – movement of ions **In a woody plant** • A ring of bark (the tissue containing phloem), was removed from a stem. • Water containing radioactive phosphate was added to the soil. • The distribution of radioactivity was traced. • There was little difference in radioactivity between a ringed and a non-ringed plant.	Movement of ions was not affected by removal of phloem. Ions move in the xylem vessels.
Ringing – movement of solutes **In a woody plant** • A ring of bark (the tissue containing phloem), was removed from a stem in summer. • Swelling appeared above the ring. • In winter no swelling appeared.	Solutes made in the leaves move in the phloem. **MUST REMEMBER** In winter: • no leaves • no photosynthesis • no solutes made • no solutes transported
Separation of xylem and phloem • Wax paper was used to separate the two transport tissues. • A plant photosynthesised using radioactive CO_2 provided to a leaf above the separated area. • The distribution of radioactivity was traced. • The level of radioactivity was higher at the top of the phloem and lower at the bottom.	Solutes move **from a high** concentration (source) **to a low** concentration (sink).

BLOOD AND BLOOD CELLS

Blood is a tissue composed of plasma and cells.

PLASMA

- Plasma is the liquid part of the blood.
- It transports soluble substances around the body, e.g. glucose, amino acids, hormones and minerals.
- It supplies and receives substances from body cells, and the amount of each substance in the plasma may vary.

There are several different blood components, but it is necessary to remember just four: red blood cells and three types of white blood cell.

RED BLOOD CELLS

Diagram	Feature of cell	Function
	Shape A disc, indented on both faces	Large surface area : volume ratio for rapid diffusion of oxygen and carbon dioxide
	Nucleus None present	Large internal volume, to hold the maximum volume of **haemoglobin**
	Other organelles None present	
	Haemoglobin A red pigment	Combines with oxygen to form **oxyhaemoglobin**, very readily when there is a high oxygen concentration, e.g. in the lungs
		Haemoglobin also carries some carbon dioxide. Most carbon dioxide is carried in the plasma of the blood as hydrogencarbonate ions.

MUST TAKE CARE

- A group of the same type of cells that carry out the same function is called a **tissue**.
- Other examples include: epithelial tissue, connective tissue and muscle.
- A group of several tissues fulfilling a function is call an **organ**.
- Examples of organs include obvious structures like the heart, lungs, liver; but less obvious things like arteries and veins.

WHITE BLOOD CELLS

Must recognise three different types of white blood cell.
They all have these features in common:

- None contains haemoglobin, so they are not red.
- All have a nucleus.

Diagram	Feature of cell	Function
Granulocyte	• Cytoplasm is granular. • Nucleus is lobed.	• It engulfs bacteria (by phagocytosis). • It is involved in the allergic response.
Lymphocyte	• Cytoplasm is not granular. • Nucleus is round, large and fills up almost all of the cell.	• It produces antibodies. • It is involved in the humoral immune response.
Monocyte	• Cytoplasm is not granular. • Nucleus is a kidney bean shape.	• It engulfs bacteria (by phagocytosis).

For practice in answering AS Biology questions, why not use *Collins Exam Practice AS Biology*?

EXTENDED IMMUNOLOGY

CELLULAR AND HUMORAL IMMUNITY

Cellular immunity	Humoral immunity
• This deals with pathogens that enter one of your own cells.	• This deals with pathogens that do not enter our cells.
• It uses T-lymphocytes.	• It uses B-lymphocytes.
• These are differentiated into T-killer lymphocytes.	• These produce antibodies (proteins).
	(See 'Immunology', pages 49–50)

CELLULAR IMMUNITY

STAGES OF RESPONSE TO A NON-SELF ANTIGEN PRESENT ON A CELL

When pathogens infect a cell

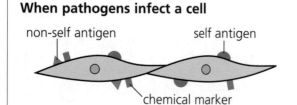

- Non-self antigens from the pathogen project from the surface of the cell.
- Human cells possess chemical markers.

Clonal expansion

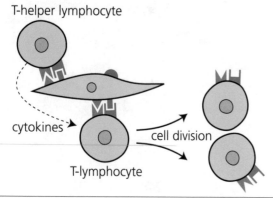

- The specific T-lymphocyte has receptors which attach to the non-self antigens only when it is next to a chemical marker.
- The specific T-helper lymphocyte binds to the antigen as well.
- The T-helper lymphocyte produces chemicals called cytokines.
- Cytokines activate the attached T-lymphocyte.
- The T-lymphocyte divides, producing a clone.
- Thus, many identical T-lymphocytes are produced.

Differentiation

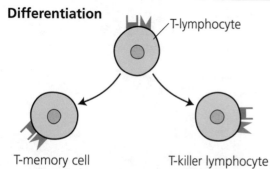

The cloned T-lymphocytes differentiate into:
- either T-killer lymphocytes which destroy any of your own cells which display the non-self antigen.
- or T-memory lymphocytes which are stored in lymphatic tissue. They rapidly divide to form many of this type of T-killer lymphocyte when exposed to the same non-self antigen again.

MUST REMEMBER

Cellular immunity is also activated by cells or organs that have come from a different person, e.g. in a transplant.

In a transplant, the cells will have non-self antigens on their surface.

TYPES OF IMMUNITY

Active immunity

Definition: An individual's immune system is stimulated to make B-lymphocytes and T-lymphocytes specific to a non-self antigen. The immune system stores specific memory cells.

Passive immunity

Definition: The individual is given antibodies.

How do you meet the antigen?	How do you get the antibody?
Natural active immunity • You get the disease, – but there is the risk of it being fatal. **Artificial active immunity** The non-self antigen is artificially introduced into the body as: 1. the dead pathogen. The immune system is not fully stimulated as the organism is not dividing. The dead pathogen will not give life-long immunity, but requires a booster, e.g. cholera vaccine. 2. the live but weakened pathogen. The immune system is fully stimulated as the introduced pathogen is alive and reproducing. It often gives life-long immunity, e.g. TB vaccine. 3. the extracted antigen. The immune system is not fully stimulated as only the non-self antigen is introduced. It will not give life-long immunity, but requires annual repeated doses, e.g. flu vaccine.	**Natural passive immunity** This is gained: • through the placenta. • in breast milk. **Artificial passive immunity** This is gained: • by injected antibodies specific to the non-self antigen.
Result Active immunity takes time to develop but lasts a long time due to the formation of memory cells.	**Result** Passive immunity gives instant protection but lasts a short time as the antibodies are destroyed and are not replaced.

BLOOD CLOTTING

Blood clotting:
- stops loss of blood.
- stops entry of pathogens.

When a blood vessel is cut, collagen is exposed and platelets respond by releasing chemicals:
- **serotonin**. This stimulates the muscles in the blood vessel to contract and restrict the flow of blood.
- **thromboplastin**. This stimulates the body to begin the process of forming a blood clot.

The blood contains two soluble proteins involved in the clotting mechanism:
- **prothrombin**
- **fibrinogen**.

Clotting process	Properties of clotting proteins
In the presence of **calcium ions**, thromboplastin converts **prothrombin** into **thrombin**.	Prothrombin is an **inactive enzyme**. Thrombin is an **active enzyme**.
Thrombin converts **fibrinogen** into **fibrin**.	Fibrinogen is a **soluble protein**. Fibrin is an **insoluble protein**. • It forms sticky threads that catch blood cells. • The sticky mass seals broken blood vessels.

Summary

thromboplastin and calcium ions
↓
(inactive) prothrombin ⟶ (active) thrombin
↓
(soluble) fibrinogen ⟶ (insoluble) fibrin

EFFECT OF EXERCISE

EFFECT OF EXERCISE ON THE HEART

Exercise increases **cardiac output** by increasing both **stroke volume** and **heart rate**.

$$\text{Cardiac output} = \text{stroke volume} \times \text{heart rate}$$

That is, cardiac output = the amount of blood passing out of the heart per cardiac cycle

multiplied by

how many times the heart beats per minute

No exercise/sleeping	Little exercise/sitting	Heavy exercise/running
Slower heart beat	Normal heart beat	Faster heart beat
More impulses from the **vagus nerve**	**Myogenic** control (see 'Heart and circulation', pages 21–26)	More impulses from the **accelerator nerve** Hormone effect – adrenaline
Imagine a car – **running downhill with the driver's foot on the break**.	Imagine a car – **freewheeling downhill**.	Imagine a car – **running downhill with the driver's foot on the accelerator**.

EFFECT OF EXERCISE ON THE DISTRIBUTION OF BLOOD

The amount of blood going to different organs varies when doing exercise.
This is due to:

- **vasoconstriction** – the muscles in the arterioles contract and reduce the flow of blood

- **vasodilation** – the muscles in the arterioles relax and increase the flow of blood

BLOOD SUPPLY TO ORGANS DURING EXERCISE

Increases to...	Constant to...	Decreases to...
Muscle • providing more oxygen and nutrients Skin • which removes excess heat by convection	Brain • still requires nutrients and oxygen to function when the body is under stress	Gut • digesting and absorbing nutrients is not a priority Kidney • removing waste from the blood is not a priority

EFFECT OF EXERCISE ON VENTILATION

Ventilation is controlled by the medulla (see 'The lungs and ventilation', pages 27–29) and both rate and depth of breathing are increased during exercise, with changing carbon dioxide levels in the blood.

Terms given to volumes of air in the lungs	What the terms means
Vital capacity	The **maximum** amount of air that can be exhaled, after a deep in-breath The **maximum** usable volume of the lungs **This will increase with exercise.**
Residual volume	The **air left** in the lungs after full exhalation This stops the sides of the lungs coming together. **This is still unused, even with strenuous exercise.**
Tidal volume	The volume of air taken into the lungs during a **normal breath** ... ... when the body is at rest **This will get larger and faster with exercise.**
Inspiratory reserve	The **extra** volume of air that can be **forced into** the lungs **This will get larger with exercise.**
Expiratory reserve	The **extra** volume of air that can be **forced out of** the lungs **This will get larger with exercise.**

A trace on a **spirometer** shows the different breathing patterns:

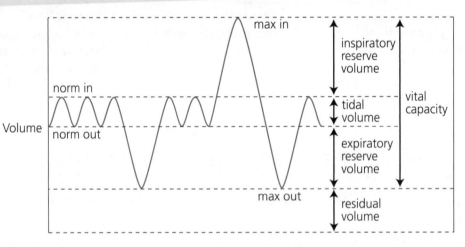

EFFECT ON INHALATION AND EXHALATION

Breathing	Inhalation	Exhalation
At rest	External intercostal muscles contract: • ribs **pulled** up and out	External intercostal muscles relax: • ribs move down and in, due to recoil of rib cage
During exercise	External intercostal muscles contract: • ribs **pulled** up and out	Internal intercostal muscles relax: • ribs move down and in, due to recoil of rib cage Internal intercostal muscles contract: • ribs **pulled** down and in **Therefore, as exhalation is faster, the next breath starts earlier.**

MUST TAKE CARE

At rest the ribs are **not** moved down by the contraction of the internal intercostal muscles.

Movement down happens passively when the cartilage in the rib cage recoils as the external intercostal muscles are relaxed. The internal intercostal muscles are used only in exercise.

PATHOGENIC MICRO-ORGANISMS

HOW MICRO-ORGANISMS GAIN ENTRY

Pathogens must be able to overcome the body's protective mechanisms which include:

- physical barriers
- chemical barriers.

Physical barrier	Properties and action of barrier	How pathogens enter
Skin	<ul><li>Layered</li><li>**Keratin**-impregnated surface cells</li><li>Dead surface cells which break away</li></ul> Pathogens cannot enter through intact skin.	Bacteria can enter when the skin is broken. Insects such as mosquitoes pierce the skin and can act as vectors for pathogens.
Respiratory system	<ul><li>Cells which line the trachea and bronchus produce **mucus** and are **ciliated**.</li></ul> Mucus traps pathogens and the cilia move them to the throat where they will be swallowed and killed by the acid contents in the stomach.	Influenza virus and TB bacteria can penetrate the thin mucus membranes.

Chemical barrier	Properties and action of barrier	How pathogens enter
Sebum – produced by sebaceous gland in skin	<ul><li>Lowers pH</li></ul> Low pH inhibits micro-organism growth.	
Sweat – produced by sweat gland in skin	<ul><li>Contains **lysozyme**</li></ul> This is an enzyme that digests bacteria.	
Tears – produced by tear glands	<ul><li>Contains **lysozyme**</li></ul> This is an enzyme that digests bacteria.	
Acid – produced by the vagina	<ul><li>Lowers pH a lot</li></ul> The acid kills micro-organisms.	HIV can penetrate thin mucus membranes.
Acid – produced by the stomach	<ul><li>Lowers pH a lot</li></ul> The acid kills micro-organisms.	Bacteria causing cholera can survive the stomach acid and infect the intestine.

If pathogens enter, the body reacts with a **non-specific response** known as **inflammation**. **Histamine** is released by white blood cells which causes:

- more blood to enter the area – vasodilation.
- capillaries to become more permeable.
- white blood cells to be attracted to the area.

A **specific response** follows due to the activity of white blood cells.
(See 'Immunology', pages 49–50, and 'Extended immunology', pages 84–85.)

IS A DISEASE THE RESULT OF A MICRO-ORGANISM?

Koch's postulate states that:

If all of the following questions can be answered 'yes', then the disease is caused by a micro-organism.

- Is the micro-organism present in the diseased organisms and not present in healthy ones?

- Can the micro-organism be isolated from the infected organism and grown in culture?

- When the micro-organism is introduced into a healthy organism, will it cause the disease?

- Can the micro-organism be isolated from the new host?

HOW MICRO-ORGANISMS CAUSE DISEASE

Physical damage to the cell	Toxin release affecting the cell
Some pathogens destroy cells: • Viruses, e.g. HIV, kill T-helper lymphocytes (see 'Extended immunology, pages 84–85).	As they grow, some pathogens release chemicals called **exotoxins**: • e.g. the bacterium that causes diphtheria. The toxin blocks protein synthesis.
• *Plasmodium* is the parasite that causes malaria: it destroys red blood cells.	When they die, some pathogens release chemicals called **endotoxins**: • e.g. *Salmonella*, the bacterium that causes food poisoning. The toxin breaks down the membrane of the intestinal cells.

GRAPH OF BACTERIAL GROWTH

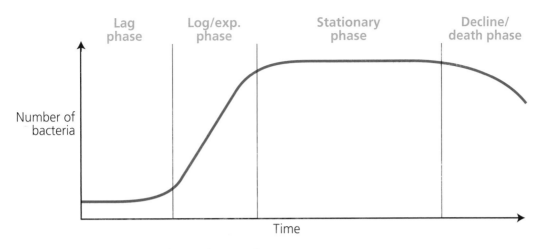

Phase	What is happening
Lag phase	The bacterial cells adapt to the new environment by making enzymes.
	Cells may increase in size during this time, but do not divide.
Log/ exponential phase	Cell division occurs.
	This stage is called logarithmic or exponential because the bacterial cell number continually doubles: $2 \rightarrow 4 \rightarrow 8 \rightarrow 16 \rightarrow 32 \rightarrow 64 \rightarrow 128 \rightarrow 256$ etc
Stationary phase	The rate at which new cells are formed by cell division is balanced by the rate of cell death.
	Cell death occurs because of: • a lack of nutrients, due to their being taken up into cells during log-phase growth, • or a build-up of toxins, due to toxin release during log-phase growth.
Decline/death phase	The rate of bacterial cells dying is greater than the rate at which they are produced by cell division.
	This phase occurs because cells can only survive exposure to harsh conditions (e.g. few nutrients or too many toxins) for a brief period of time.

FACTORS THAT AFFECT THE GROWTH OF MICRO-ORGANISMS

These include:

- nutrients
- pH
- oxygen concentration
- temperature
- presence of other micro-organisms.

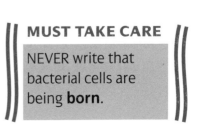

MUST TAKE CARE

NEVER write that bacterial cells are being **born**.

THE STRUCTURE OF HIV AND ITS REPLICATION

Human Immunodeficiency Virus is the cause of the condition known as
AIDS or **Acquired Immunodeficiency Syndrome**.

STRUCTURE OF THE VIRUS

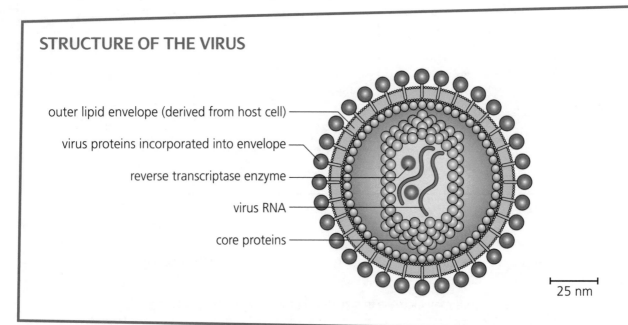

outer lipid envelope (derived from host cell)

virus proteins incorporated into envelope

reverse transcriptase enzyme

virus RNA

core proteins

25 nm

THE COURSE OF INFECTION

Stages in the life cycle of HIV	More detail
Protein in the virus envelope **attaches to a specific protein** in the membrane of the cell being invaded.	• The attaching protein is specific to T-helper lymphocytes and a few other cells.
Virus membrane fuses with the host cell membrane.	• The cell is infected.
Virus RNA and enzymes are passed into the cell.	One of the enzymes is **reverse transcriptase** which causes virus RNA to be made into virus DNA.
Virus DNA enters the nucleus and joins the host cells DNA.	• The virus remains dormant. The body responds to virus non-self antigens and produces antibodies. The antibodies can be detected in the blood and the infected person is described as **HIV positive**.
Many years later: The virus DNA is **transcribed**. The virus DNA is **translated**. The virus parts are **assembled**.	• New virus RNA is made. • New virus proteins are made, i.e. enzymes and proteins of the capsid (the virus coat).
New viruses break out of the cell.	• New viruses use the host cell membrane to coat their cells.
The host cell is destroyed.	• The T-helper lymphocyte is destroyed. • So the total number of lymphocytes decreases. • The body is unable to destroy pathogens – the immune system is damaged. AIDS is the result of opportunistic micro-organisms which enter the body while the immune system is damaged.

PARASITES

Parasitism is a feeding relationship between two organisms:

- The **parasite** – gains from the relationship.
- The **host** – does not.

A parasite must:

- maintain its position in or on the host.
- resist the host's attempts to destroy it.
- reproduce so that the offspring can find a suitable habitat in which to develop.

ADAPTATIONS OF HUMAN PARASITES

Adaptation	Parasite	Parasite
	Plasmodium, **a protozoon that causes the disease** malaria	*Schistosoma*, **a blood fluke that causes the disease** bilharzia
Ability to penetrate the host	Injected by a **mosquito**, which is the **vector**.	One stage of the life cycle bores through the skin.
Means of attachment to the host	No special requirements are needed as it circulates in the blood of the host.	The adult fluke lives in veins near the bladder. Suckers help it to attach to the walls of the vein.
Avoiding the host's defence mechanism	It 'hides' from the white blood cells by being inside the host's cells.	The parasite makes substances that switch off the host's immune system. It does this by coating itself with molecules from host's red blood cells.
Development of reproductive strategies	Reproduction occurs in 4 stages of its life cycle, producing extremely large numbers – 30 000 per mm^3.	A large number of eggs are produced from each adult. From 1 egg, 200 000 larvae can be produced.
Complex life cycle	Two hosts: Primary host – human Secondary host – mosquito The mosquito is the vector and allows the transfer from primary host to secondary host.	Two hosts: Primary host – human Secondary host – water snail The water snail is the vector and allows the transfer from primary host to secondary host.
Reduction of body systems	Has no locomotory system: – Living inside the host's cells, it does not have to move to find food.	It does not have a complex nervous system – conditions in host are constant. It has no locomotory system.

PARASITES GENERALLY HAVE A COMPLEX LIFE CYCLE

- Parasites lay **many eggs**.
- They have many **different larval stages** in their life cycle.
- Each stage is adapted to one role.
- Each stage may be able to **reproduce asexually**.
- They may have a **secondary host**.

LIFE CYCLES

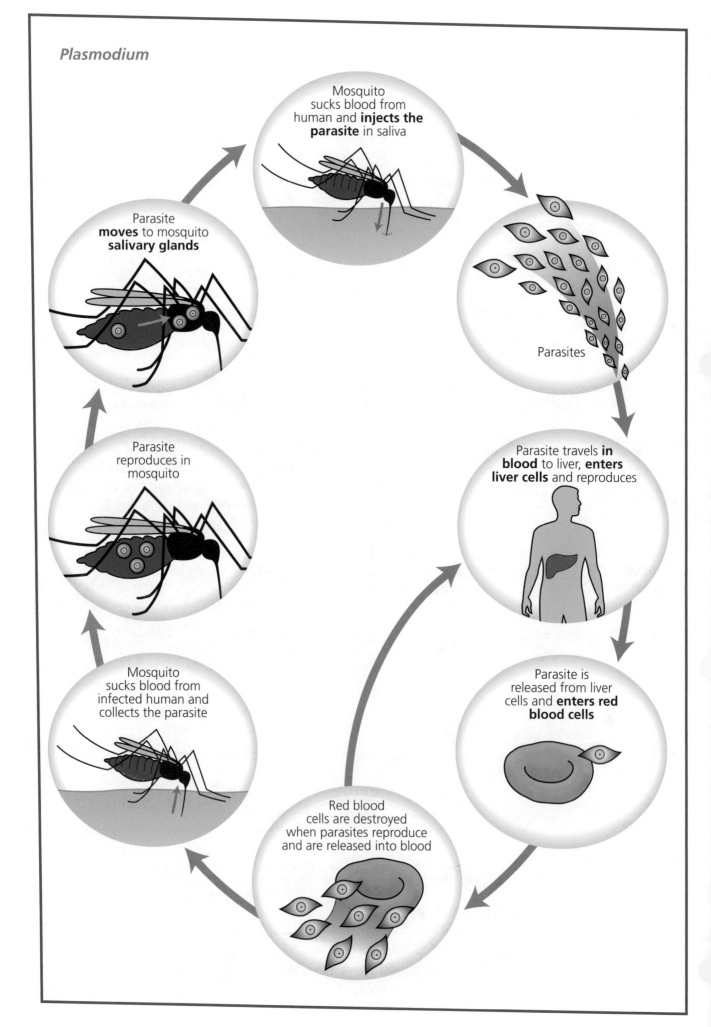

Plasmodium

Mosquito sucks blood from human and **injects the parasite** in saliva

Parasite **moves** to mosquito **salivary glands**

Parasites

Parasite reproduces in mosquito

Parasite travels **in blood** to liver, **enters liver cells** and reproduces

Mosquito sucks blood from infected human and collects the parasite

Parasite is released from liver cells and **enters red blood cells**

Red blood cells are destroyed when parasites reproduce and are released into blood

Schistosoma

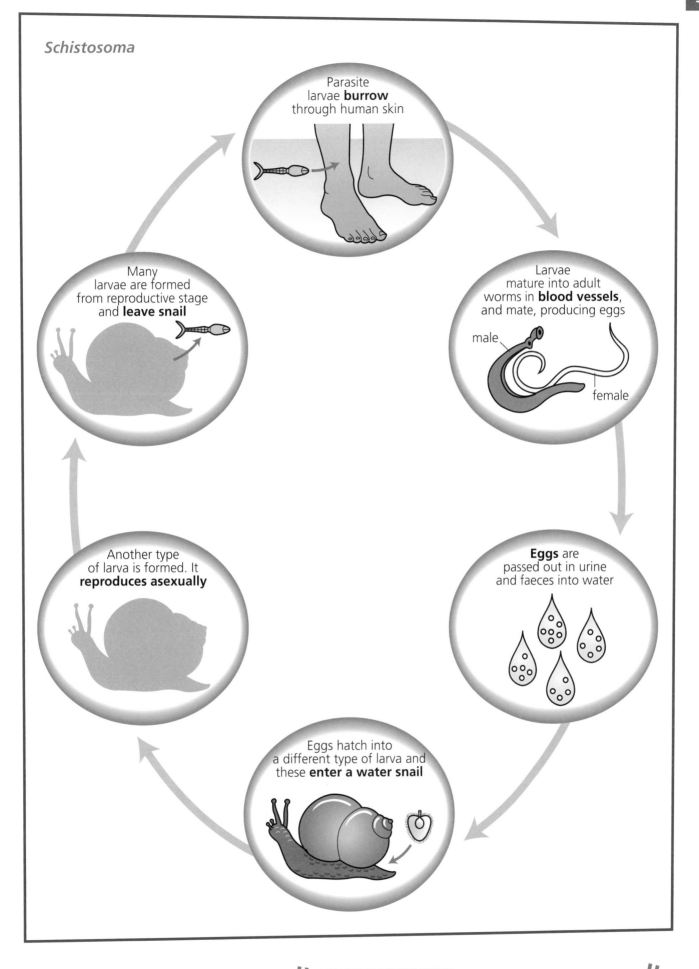

Parasite larvae **burrow** through human skin

Larvae mature into adult worms in **blood vessels**, and mate, producing eggs

male

female

Many larvae are formed from reproductive stage and **leave snail**

Eggs are passed out in urine and faeces into water

Another type of larva is formed. It **reproduces asexually**

Eggs hatch into a different type of larva and these **enter a water snail**

MUST REMEMBER

There are many different stages in each life cycle and each has a different name.

Must *not* learn the names of the individual stages.

HEART DISEASE

HOW A NORMAL HEART WORKS

- The heart is a pump made from **cardiac muscle**.
- When this muscle contracts, enough pressure is created to move blood through the heart and into arteries.
- The heart muscle is **respiring** to provide the energy to contract. This requires a supply of oxygen and glucose.
- The blood that is moved through the heart does NOT supply the heart muscle with its oxygen or glucose.
- The heart muscle must get its oxygen and glucose like any other muscle, from a capillary network.
- Blood is supplied to capillaries from arteries.
- So the heart must have its own arterial supply. This is provided by **coronary arteries**.
- The coronary arteries take blood directly from the aorta.

CORONARY HEART DISEASE (CHD)

Angina	Myocardial infarction
• The coronary arteries may get **partly blocked**.	• The coronary arteries may become **fully blocked**.
• Then the heart muscle will get less oxygen.	• Then this part of the heart receives no oxygen.
• The heart will now respire **anaerobically**.	• Some of the muscle dies.
• This produces the waste product **lactate**.	• If lots of the muscle dies, so could you!!
• The build-up of lactate causes chest pain.	

ATHEROSCLEROSIS

Atherosclerosis is a disease in which the **lumen** of the artery becomes narrower. Narrowing is caused by damage to the inner layer of the artery, the **endothelium**.

Progress of atherosclerosis	Appearance of artery
An artery is made up of three layers. • Outer layer – **connective tissue** • Middle layer – **muscle and connective tissue** • Inner layer – **endothelium**, made of epithelial cells	

Progress of atherosclerosis	Appearance of artery
• The endothelium may become damaged. • If this happens, fats, in the form of lipoproteins, are taken up from the blood. • A mass of cells, full of fat, builds up between the muscle layer and the endothelium of an artery. This mass of fat-laden cells is called an atheroma.	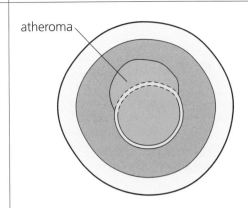 atheroma
• Muscle cells and fibres grow into the atheroma. • This forms a plaque. • As a plaque grows, it bulges into the lumen of the artery. • This narrows the lumen. This condition is called atherosclerosis.	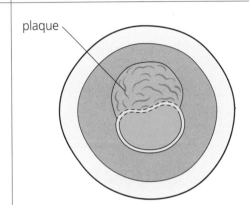 plaque
• If the plaque gets very large, it can tear the endothelium. • A blood clot may form at the site of the tear. • The blood clot is called a thrombus. • The formation of a blood clot in a blood vessel is called thrombosis.	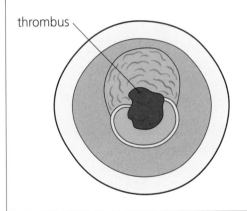 thrombus

The blood clot could:

• cause pressure to build up, breaking the artery. If this occurs in the brain it is the cause of a stroke.

• break free and completely block a small artery, causing surrounding cells to die. If this occurs in the heart it causes a myocardial infarction.

MUST TAKE CARE

There are many new words that have a specific meaning.

• Must make a list of these new words with short definitions.

• Must learn them as they must be used correctly in the exam.

WHAT FACTORS CAUSE HEART DISEASE?

There are a number of factors that increase the risk of **coronary heart disease**, CHD.

Risks you can avoid	Risks you cannot avoid
• Cigarette smoking • High blood cholesterol levels • High blood pressure • Obesity • Lack of exercise	• Old age • Being male • Inheritance • Diabetes

Many of the factors influence one another.

• Nicotine in cigarette smoke cause the muscles in arteries to contract, which increases blood pressure.

• Old age may reduce the amount of exercise taken, which may contribute to increased weight gain.

SOME RISKS IN MORE DETAIL

Risk	Notes
Tobacco smoking	• **Carbon monoxide** reduces the ability of the red blood cells to carry oxygen, which seems to increase the risk of damaging the endothelium. • **Nicotine** narrows arteries, leading to increased blood pressure.
Blood cholesterol **Cholesterol** is a type of lipid. It combines with protein, forming lipoproteins.	• **Low density lipoproteins** (LDL) carry high levels of cholesterol and increase the risk of developing atheromas. • **High density lipoproteins** (HDL) have low levels of cholesterol and can mop up cholesterol from LDL. They do not contribute to atheromas.
High blood pressure Several factors lead to increased blood pressure: • Stress • Obesity • Alcohol • Tobacco smoking • Salt	• There is only a problem when blood pressure is high over a long period of time. • The artery responds to high blood pressure by increasing its muscle layer. • This causes the lumen to narrow. • The pressure is increased further. • This results in damage to the endothelium. • Therefore the risk of an atheroma forming is increased.

CANCER

Cancer is a number of diseases with one thing in common:

- Cells grow and divide, and do not stop.

Normal cell growth

- During growth or repair, cells divide, by mitosis, but then stop.
- This is regulated by genes.

Uncontrolled cell growth

- When certain genes undergo a mutation, they can cause the cell to lose control of its division.
- These genes are called **oncogenes**.

GENERAL FEATURES OF CELL GROWTH

Normal cell growth	Uncontrolled cell growth
Gene	Gene mutation
↓	↓
It codes for the synthesis of a **protein**.	Cell does not respond to signals from other cells.
↓	↓
The effect is that the cell divides and grows.	Continuous mitosis occurs.
↓	↓
Cells stop dividing.	Tumour forms.

Specific examples

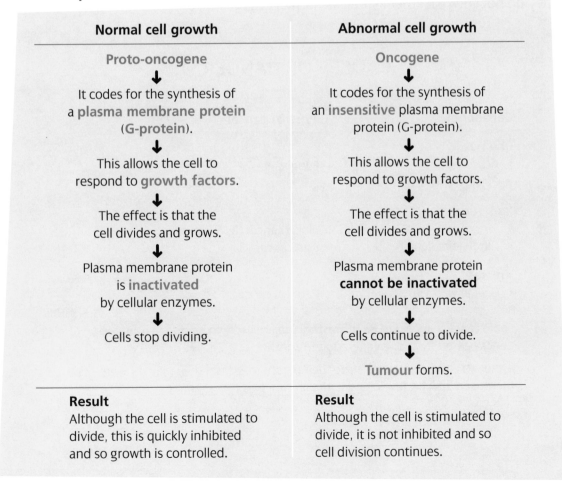

Normal cell growth	Abnormal cell growth
Proto-oncogene	Oncogene
↓	↓
It codes for the synthesis of a **plasma membrane protein** **(G-protein)**.	It codes for the synthesis of an **insensitive** plasma membrane protein (G-protein).
↓	↓
This allows the cell to respond to **growth factors**.	This allows the cell to respond to growth factors.
↓	↓
The effect is that the cell divides and grows.	The effect is that the cell divides and grows.
↓	↓
Plasma membrane protein is **inactivated** by cellular enzymes.	Plasma membrane protein **cannot be inactivated** by cellular enzymes.
↓	↓
Cells stop dividing.	Cells continue to divide.
	↓
	Tumour forms.
Result Although the cell is stimulated to divide, this is quickly inhibited and so growth is controlled.	**Result** Although the cell is stimulated to divide, it is not inhibited and so cell division continues.

TUMOUR SUPPRESSOR GENES

- **Tumour suppressor genes** stop cell division.
- Cancerous cells may have a **mutated** form of this gene which fails to stop cell division.

TUMOURS CAN BE BENIGN OR MALIGNANT

Benign tumours	Malignant tumours
<ul><li>They are a mass of cells.</li><li>They do not destroy other tissues in the body.</li><li>They may press on blood vessels or nerves, reducing their normal function.</li></ul>	<ul><li>They are a mass of cells from which cells break off.</li></ul>These cells:<ul><li>move in the blood or lymph.</li><li>invade other tissues.</li><li>form **secondary tumours** in other organs, damaging other tissue.</li></ul>This process is called **metastasis**.

Cancer cells can be recognised as:

- they are generally larger than normal cells.
- their nuclei take up more space in the cell than normal.
- they fail to differentiate (do not become specialised).
- they do not stick together as well as normal cells.

CAUSES OF CANCER

Carcinogen	Type of cancer
Chemicals<ul><li>Asbestos</li><li>Cigarette smoke</li></ul>	Lung cancer
Radiation<ul><li>X-rays</li><li>Ultra-violet light</li></ul>	Blood cancer (leukaemia) Skin cancer
Viruses<ul><li>Genital wart virus</li></ul>	Cervical cancer

Some cancers appear to be **inherited** and are likely to be due to mutated genes passed from one generation to another.

Although children may not have their parent's disease, they may have an **increased risk** of developing it. Breast cancer is one example.

DIAGNOSIS OF DISEASE

The meaning of diagnosis: **A diagnosis identifies a disease or condition.**

SOME DIAGNOSTIC TESTS

Type of test	Detail
• Biochemical tests	Blood or urine is tested.
• Immunological tests	Tests use monoclonal antibodies.
• Biopsies	Samples of tissues are looked at.
• Cytological examination	Microscopic examination is made of a few cells.
• Culturing micro-organisms	Culture is from blood, urine, faeces, mucus.
• Genetic analysis	The genes, often of fetal cells, are looked at.
• X-rays	Damage to bones and soft tissue is seen.
• Ultrasound	High frequency sound waves are reflected from the body and converted into a visual image.
• Endoscopy	Fibre optics allow a view inside the body.

GENETIC ANALYSIS

DNA probes can be used to identify genes associated with a disease.

Process	What happens
DNA is cut up.	**Restriction enzymes** are used to cut the DNA into different size pieces.
Pieces are separated.	**Electrophoresis** separates the different-sized fragments of DNA.
A probe is added.	A **probe** is: • **a single strand of DNA**. • made up of nucleotides which are **complementary** to a sequence of bases in a gene. • labelled, **radioactively** or with a **fluorescent marker**.
A probe is attached.	• The DNA is carefully warmed to break the hydrogen bonds between the bases. • The probe will attach to the open double strand of DNA. As the probe is labelled, the gene is now marked.

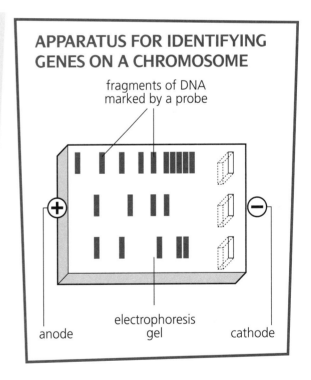

APPARATUS FOR IDENTIFYING GENES ON A CHROMOSOME

fragments of DNA marked by a probe

anode   electrophoresis gel   cathode

BIOCHEMICAL TESTS

These can be use to identify changes in concentration and distribution of enzymes in the blood and other tissues.

DIAGNOSING PANCREATITIS

Pancreatitis is a disease of the pancreas.

The pancreas is an organ that normally produces digestive enzymes which are sent to the gut:

• **Amylase** breaks down starch into maltose.
• **Lipase** breaks down lipids into fatty acids and glycerol.
• **Trypsin** (a protease) breaks down protein to peptides.

What happens when the pancreas is functioning normally	What happens when the pancreas is diseased
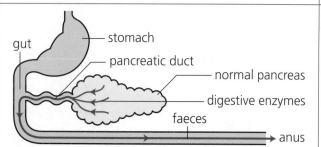	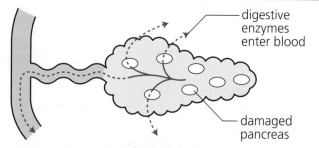
• The pancreas secretes digestive enzymes into the gut. • Some of these enzymes are lost in the faeces.	• Pancreatic cells break down. • Digestive enzymes are released into the blood. • Less enzymes are found in the faeces.

Diagnosis
• Amylase, lipase and trypsin can be detected in the blood.
• Lower than normal levels of these enzymes are found in the faeces.

MUST TAKE CARE

The pancreas also produces insulin which **is** released directly into the blood.

BIOSENSORS

• **Biosensors** contain enzymes which each react with a specific substance in the body.
• The 'quantity' of this substance can be measured.

Enzymes are used in biosensors because:
• enzymes are sensitive.
• small amounts of substrate can be identified.
• enzymes are specific.
• only one substance is identified.

DETECTING GLUCOSE

• The biosensor is a plastic strip containing **two enzymes**,
• and a **dye**.
• The plastic strip is dipped into a sample of urine or blood.

Step one • Glucose is joined to oxygen using the enzyme **glucose oxidase**, which produces gluconic acid and hydrogen peroxide.	
Summary equation	glucose oxidase ↓ glucose + oxygen + water → gluconic acid + hydrogen peroxide
Step two • The second enzyme, **peroxidase**, breaks down hydrogen peroxide, changing the colour of the dye.	
Summary equation	peroxidase ↓ dye + hydrogen peroxide → water + different colour of dye
Step three • The colour can be related to the concentration of glucose in the urine (or blood).	

Example: Diastix urine glucose test strip (dipstick) and colour chart

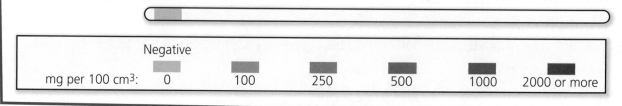

	Negative					
mg per 100 cm^3:	0	100	250	500	1000	2000 or more

DRUGS TO TREAT DISEASE

BETA BLOCKERS

Beta blockers are used to help people who:
- have high blood pressure and angina.
- suffer from stress.

Beta receptors are protein molecules in the membrane of:
- muscle cells in arteries.
- the sinoatrial node (SAN) of the heart.

Without beta blockers	The hormone **adrenaline** is produced when the heart is required to beat faster. • It travels to the heart in the blood. When the hormone adrenaline combines with the beta receptors: • the muscle cells in the arteries contract and pressure inside the arteries increases. • the heart contracts faster and harder and the blood pressure increases.
With beta blockers	Beta blockers have a **similar shape to adrenaline**. • They can fit into the beta receptor. • This **stops adrenaline linking** with them. This **lowers** blood pressure.

ANTIBIOTICS

What are antibiotics?	Why are they produced naturally?
A chemical made by bacteria or fungi that harms or kills bacteria is called an **antibiotic**.	**Antibiotics are produced to destroy competitors**. • We can collect antibiotics from bacteria or fungi that we culture. • Many antibiotics are now artifically made with similar chemical structures to the naturally occurring types.

WHY IS A BACTERIAL INFECTION A PROBLEM?

Bacterial cells divide very quickly, much faster than plant or animal cells.
- Bacteria produce waste products which can be toxic (poisonous) – **endotoxins**.
- Bacteria die, releasing toxic products – **exotoxins**.

Both endotoxins and exotoxins damage animal cells and cause disease.

MUST TAKE CARE

Not to confuse **antibiotic** with **antibody** or **antigen**.

(See Immunology, pages 49–50 and be clear about the difference.)

Example of an antibiotic

Penicillin is:
- made by the fungus *Penicillium*.
- produced industrially in large fermenters.

Effect	Type of antibiotic
• Some antibiotics slow down bacterial growth.	Bacteriostatic
• Some antibiotics kill bacteria. Some kill only a few bacteria – **narrow-spectrum**, e.g. Penicillin. Some kill lots of different bacteria – **broad-spectrum**, e.g. Chloramphenicol.	Bacteriocidal

HOW DO ANTIBIOTICS WORK?

Effect of antibiotics	Explanation
Prevent **bacterial cell walls** forming, e.g. Penicillin	The bacterial cytoplasm contains solutes. Cytoplasm has a lower water potential than the outside medium. Water has the tendency to enter the cell by osmosis. As water enters, the absence of cell walls allows the cell to expand unchecked, and it eventually bursts.
Prevent **transcription**, e.g. Actinomycin	No mRNA is made from the template of DNA. Protein cannot be made. The cell dies.
Prevents **translation**, e.g. Erythromycin and Tetracycline	mRNA is not translated in the ribosomes. Protein cannot be made. The cell dies.
Prevents **replication**, e.g. Sulphonamides	DNA is not copied. Mitosis and cell division stops. New cells cannot be made.

MONOCLONAL ANTIBODIES

An **antibody** is:
- a protein produced by a B-lymphocyte,
- in response to a non-self antigen that enters the body.

Each B-lymphocyte produces only one type of antibody.

- If such a cell is isolated and allowed to divide, it produces a **clone** of 'identical' B-lymphocytes.
- These B-lymphocytes produce many of just one type of antibody: **monoclonal antibodies**.

> **MUST REMEMBER**
>
> The effects of antibiotics are specific to bacterial cells, so antibiotics do not harm animal cells.

USING A FLUORESCENT MONOCLONAL ANTIBODY TO MARK CELLS

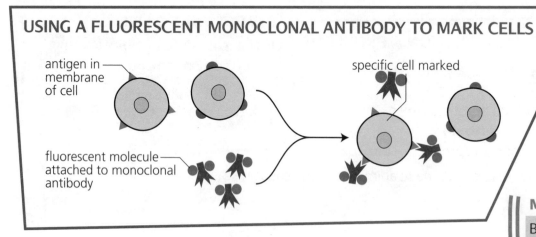

antigen in membrane of cell

specific cell marked

fluorescent molecule attached to monoclonal antibody

USES OF MONOCLONAL ANTIBODIES

> **MUST REMEMBER**
>
> B-lymphocytes differentiate into plasma cells.
>
> It is the plasma cells that actually produce antibodies.

Purpose	Detail
• Pregnancy testing	The hormone **human chorionic gonadotrophin** (hCG), which is produced only in pregnancy, can be detected.
• Drug testing	This uses ELISA – enzyme-linked immunosorbant assay.
• The magic bullet idea	If cancer cells have different antigens from ordinary cells, then it may be possible to treat cancer by targeting only the cancer cells in the body: • Poison is attached to antibodies which build up only in the cancer cells and kill them. • The poison has no effect on ordinary cells which have different antigens.

INDEX